Imaginary Portrait of an Art Historian

J.J. HALADYN

Imaginary Portrait of an Art Historian

EYECORNER PRESS

Published by EyeCorner Press in the series 100.
November 2022, Agger, Denmark.
Designed and typeset by Camelia Elias.
Images © JJ. Haladyn; on pp. 13, 43, and 71 by kind permission.
ISBN 978-87-92633-89-7

www.eyecorner.press

Illustrations

Contents

40 Fragments

1 The Study

They have been renovating the art historian's study. That delightful, overtly modest space tucked away within a typically Italian second floor *appartamento* in a wonderful little neighborhood downtown Florence, across the street from, or at least at a close distance to their favourite restaurant, Pepo. Among old and new books, among odd prints and reproductions, some framed and hung on the walls—at times hidden behind a stack or more of books—or leaning against books on a shelf, some lying loose on surfaces or propped up against one or another object, or even captured between books or in other miscellaneous locations, many buried within strata of knowledge, some never to be found; among these books and prints and other objects, evidence of what we refer to as a history of the study of art. The art historian stands, waiting.

2   The Study

They have been renovating the art historian's study. That delightful, modest space in which many an idea was materialized and sent out into the world. I recall being shown a photograph of the study, filled with an impossible volume of books—books of all sizes on shelves and tables, stacked on the ground, books that are so beautiful and books literally falling apart. Looking at this photograph, shared with me by a close friend who had worked with the art historian, I knew I had taken too long in my examination of the document. I scanned the photograph thoroughly, looking for traces of readable titles on visible covers and spines. I recall two. The first was Timothy Verdon's pamphlet *Caravaggio e l'avventura della fede,* published by Edizioni Musei Vaticani, which was visible on the floor near the waste basket. Its cover was bent, with a hard crease running the upper third of its surface, a wound that obviously was not recent (one could see the way the image on its cover had, from this compression point, started to peel away). The second was a beautiful two volume set, *Isabella D'Este Marchioness of Mantua 1474-1539: A Study of the Renaissance* by Julia Cartwright; dark blue hardcover books with wonderful floral patterning that rested comfortably on one corner of the art historian's large wooden desk, the second volume on top with both spines visible from the study's doorway—the photograph was taken from around this spot.

It was easy for me to recognize these particular books because I own the exact edition of the title—1903, published by John Murray, London; (except my copies had the added feature of off white dust jackets that appear to have been taken from the 1932 edition of this work: the size is slightly smaller than the 1903 books and the rear blurb includes an advert for the cheap edition of Axel Munthe's *Story of San Michele*). I have seen one other photograph of the study.

Plate 1: Books in the study

This one taken as the art historian moved into the current space; we see books stacked high, arranged in two mass groupings on each side of the modest room, with a mildly narrow isle down the centre defined by the architecture of books. The woman who took this picture tells a story of the art historian, who allowed her and other students entrance into the study under the condition that they help carry books from the old study to the new, with the new one located two floors below in the same building. She talked of her surprise when witnessing this mass of paper and words, and she took the photograph as evidence of the encounter; she did, in fact, with other students, help the art historian move. When asked if any particular books stood out in her memory she answered without hesitation: Svetlana Alpers' *Roof Life,* an unusual manuscript that exists as a kind of self-portrait, or perhaps several self-portraits. Published by Yale University Press, the author takes *distant and therefore distinctive* views as she locates herself in and through her encounters with place, history and art.

Hearing the story behind this photograph of the art historian's study, of the books and objects that comprise its substance and form, I cannot help but think of the question of distance, how particular art objects ask their viewers to position themselves either *near* or *distant* (or in between) to that which is being apprehended by the visual faculties. A condition I fear we have all but forgotten in current considerations of such art historical encounters.

3 Saint Jerome in His Study

In Antonello da Messina's painting of Saint Jerome, completed around 1474 or 1475, we see the renowned theologian and historian sitting in an open-space study surrounded by his famous library. This almost stand-alone study is located within a larger architectural environment, our view of which is framed by an arched doorway that limits and focuses what we witness. The scene includes Jerome's lion, strolling on a patterned floor that reaches into the background of the fictive room; on a stair in the foreground we are also shown two birds in profile, on the left a partridge (truth) and a rather curious peacock (immortality) on the right.

Reflecting a Renaissance fascination with defining inner and outer worlds, the artist allows us to see through the windows in the back of this structure; in the lower ones a landscape and sky with birds in the upper ones, which help define the interiority of much of the representation. But the painting's focus is unmistakably on the rather peculiar study. A large writing desk is part of the architecture that, open on two sides and without a ceiling, includes the walls that define this fractional space; this study is also its own raised platform and arching extension that may—we cannot actually see—connect it to the larger architectonics of the building that contains it. There is a stage-like quality to this structure that puts the activities of the historian on display and makes obvious the foundational role of scholarship for Saint Jerome. As an early desert father, he was to, as he writes, *cut himself off from home and parents, and sister and kin and what is harder than these, the habit of exquisite dining while in the desert for five years, but the library I had built up with such ardour and pains in Rome, I could not*

15

bring myself to do without. Isolating himself from civilization, the future saint could not part with his books, literally carrying his library with him as he walked the desert. Jerome becomes the patron saint of biblical scholars, librarians, students and translators.

Of the many depictions of the saint, there is a tradition of showing him in the closed room of his study, often surrounded by his books and accompanied by his faithful lion. Albrecht Dürer's 1514 print can stand as a paradigm. Jerome is pictured in a typical 16th century German study, seated at his desk with a book in front of him, the floor at his feet ends with a step in the foreground just before which his lion and dog lay sleeping—light from windows on the side wall illuminates the room, a halo over the saint's head frames his mental engagement. In place of a closed room Messina imagines Jerome in an open construct that invites modern interpretations. Scholarship is not simply contained, architecturally or otherwise, but instead exists as an artificial separation that consciously stages its interiority. The study described in Messina's painting is not a closed world but rather a prelude to an infinite universe.

4 *Library*

Every book collection corresponds to two needs that are often also obsessions: the need to hang on to things (books), and the need to keep them in some order. Such a logic, elegantly stated, allows for a particular type of consideration of the individual whose library is being considered. In the case of the art historian we might say, as a general observation, this twofold obsession is grounded in an untimely imaginary that recognizes art's capacity to change perceptions of reality. The choice of objects, books or otherwise, reflect a sense not of the specific time and place of the library's owner (patron), not of any one history or even personage, but rather of a multifaceted identity and actuality imagined into existence.

There is an impossible logic in what is contained within this particular assemblage, which exhibits a sense and vision of art's changing relation with its own will. At times narrowly focused on a history of this object and practice we call art, at other times considering art in its dialogues with other objects and practices. Like time itself, the exactness of this or that encounter is an illusion perpetrated by the certain way books are organized, with the art historian being both an unwilling and willing accomplice. A particularly vivid example of this is the following cluster of three volumes—Laura J. Snyder's *Eye of the Beholder: Johannes Vermeer, Antoni van Leeuwenhoek, and the Reinvention of Seeing,* the catalogue *Duchamp: Re-made in Italy* and Hito Steyerl's *I Will Survive.* The encounter of such titles on a shelf may be intentional collecting on the part of the art historian, the result of one or more research projects that required such material; or it may be a serendipitous coming together of books that simply found their way into the library, such as would happen if a student of the art historian gave one as a gift; in many such encounters, both options may be in play. The fact of a book being in a library, finding itself in dialogue (material and ideational) with other such books, most often defies merely logical rationales, which are easily imposed only after the fact of their location. Instead, and the art historian is well aware of this, we must recognize in the answer that is a library the dynamic encounter of worlds of knowledge constantly imagining beyond their limits.

Plate 2: La Libreria Alfani

5   *Scholar in their Study*

The pictorial convention of painting scholars in their studies clearly emerges out of representations of Saint Jerome. Similar to this model, such depictions attempt to articulate the singular relationship of an individual, the figure of the scholar or later the scientist, to their quest for knowledge. Located most often in closed rooms, surrounded by books and other materials of their trade, as well as symbolic items that help communicate the work's meanings, these scholars are captured always at a precise moment that allows the invisible qualities of their quest, long hours of thought and inaction, to be made understandable and accessible to a viewer. Rembrandt's *A Scholar in his Study (Faust)* in The Uffizi (Inventory 6169 St. Sc.), represents a clear example of this. A scholar—some believe it to be an alchemist or the legendary Faust—is depicted in an interior, standing at a desk and by a window; he is struck by a vision of dazzling light suspended in space. Even when not as directly referenced, the qualities of the connection between scholarship and religious visions established with representations of Saint Jerome remain vital to this genre. Such a relationship between knowledge and belief is at the core of the iconography of paintings that show scholars in their studies— where a scholar's belief encounters a history of humanity's beliefs, or beliefs as a way of thinking the human.

6 San Marco

The art historian left their apartment at 10 AM on bicycle.
Stopped for a short duration at La Libreria Alfani on Via
degli Alfani, picking up two of the latest publications from
Le Edizioni Henry Beyle—Elsa Morante's *Catullo e Lesbia* (€
20,00) and Walter Benjamin's *Che cosa regalare a uno snob* (€
22,00). Arrived at San Marco around 10:45, definitely before
11 AM. Purchased an entry ticket (€ 4,00 reduced to € 2,00)
and promptly went upstairs. Past the arresting fresco of Fra
Angelico *Annunciation,* the art historian walks down the hallway of the monk cells, each with its own small wooden door
leading to an intimate space containing a small fresco. Every-
where fresh beauties meet the eye, but too numerous for men-
tion.

Fra Angelico painted frescoes in forty cells, representing the
history of Christ from nativity to death, and also the history
of the Virgin Mary. As the art historian tells it, monks would
be confined in a cell with the expectation of experiencing a
religious vision, facilitated by fasting and the imagery found
on the cell's wall. Many scenes pictured in the cells are quite
similar. There is an overwhelming sense of presence in the
manner Fra Angelico's paintings inhabit space. While essen-
tially self-contained, held within their own representational
limits, these depictions share a belief that must be embodied.
At the end of the hallway is a different space, more than just a
single room. There can be found the study of Girolamo Savon-
arola, Prior of the convent from 1489 until his violent death
in 1498. His desk remains, and on more than one visit the art
historian produced a quick sketch of the simple yet intriguing
structure of this workspace.

7 Mocking of Christ

On this particular visit the art historian was at San Marco to study the painted image in cell 7. It is located in the east corridor on the outside wall. An old wooden stool waits just inside the open doorway, placed with the intention of this visit, directly across from the fresco of *The Mocking of Christ*. The art historian sits in the cell from 12:45 to 2:05 PM. The following text was produced during this period, handwritten with blue ink in a blue marbled notebook: *I am going to tell you about last night's dream. I seemed—though I don't know the cause, since I'm not in the habit of thinking or talking about such an affair—I seemed to be visited by the spirit of the late art historian Peter Porçal. We were walking along by ourselves through an emptied San Marco, so summoning him over instantly I pointed in one cell with the fresco THE MOCKING OF CHRIST. And as I remember, that saying of André Breton came into my head right then: "The nature of his mind especially predisposed him to revising the perceptible data of time and space... At the same time, Fra Angelico does not think that a ghost can enter other than through a door." So we deliberated about this, such a quest of reality, hesitated for a while, Peter eventually decided to walk through the cell door. Standing motionless for a duration we gazed upon the vision of Christ being mocked, his tormentor consisting of several disembodied hands and one head. An intellectual vision—a type of Image Pietatis—we marvel at the collapsing of time, a simultaneity that is surreal. An art historian notes that at the lower right Saint Dominic sits reading, an action that is the eighth mode of prayer. In our dream we argue philosophically: "Is reading a surreal activity? How much of experience is borrowed experience, from so many words of other people? Don't we know that experi-*

ence produces a flat temporality, moments treated as simultaneous and splendidly personal?" Examples come to us in heaps of those who were either appreciators of art or celebrated historians of art; we are enthralled with the belief of Erwin Panofsky and his wonder at the ideas of art; we praised the inventiveness of Fra Angelico's surrealism. There came to mind the manner of his hands that hover, disconnected, cut off from body as they push and pull, pen palmed and back of hand, the same at different times and differentiated at the same time; a head without a body wears a hat as it mocks, a disembodied hand holding its hat. In short we were in such a state that now only the exact term of 'surreal' prevented us from agreement of our shared experience as Peter could not accept such a claim of Fra Angelico; and now the final cast of the die was impending, when suddenly at midnight I woke up, tormented by curiosity; a sense of intellectual satisfaction spread over my whole body. How deeply in the course of my dream was I rooted in the belief, which I persuaded myself was absolutely true when I awoke, that Peter shared a vital piece of knowledge about reality and art. Finally, I got up at the usual time—you know my habit—and after a moment of self-reflection, I took pen in hand as usual, and this dream which had uplifted my spirit presented itself to me now that I roused. So I am making you a partner in my thoughts, since you seemed to be a partner in my dream. Farewell and to be happy, drive away superfluous perceptions! January 14 at dawn.

Plate 3: The Mocking of Christ

8 Coffee with Peter

I first met Peter Porçal in a small café in Florence. It was November 2013, the day of my fortieth birthday. Though geographically impossible, since it could not have been where I imagine, and in spite of evidence that the café in the imagined location is not the correct one, I persist in remembering this encounter up the street from the Museo Galileo. In the back, behind the bar, a small room filled with tables awkwardly organized. Miriam and I arrived to find our friends, the artists Andy Patton, Jamelie Hassan and Ron Benner already seated, decidedly on the left-hand side of the space near the windows. And with them an older man, Peter, who was in poor health—in the middle of a story, he kept pausing attempting to catch his breath. He had an obvious presence, drawing attention to himself without much effort, by the way he spoke or listened or drank his beer.

Knowing him very little at that moment, it was clear that he chose his words and gestures with extreme care. Arriving with our coffees, we were immediately swept up in the torrent of his story telling, which seemed to have a life of its own. While I cannot be sure, it felt as if Peter chose some of what he shared—real or fabulous, it did not matter—based on my intrigue, questions and general expressions of interest. Many were stories about the history of art and his life as an art historian. I hear of his education and early career, working with Horst Waldemar Janson who wore *thick* gold chains and earned the nickname *the horse* (I can still picture Peter's gesture when he said these words, slightly deepening his voice and leaning forward, accentuating his nose). Peter expresses his admiration for Erwin Panofsky—Panofsky's approach to art as much as his refusal to accept an honour from the German government because, as a German Jew, he could not accept the hypocrisy. Yet Peter also talked to me about the Russian filmmaker Andrei Tarkovsky, who lived in the building beside his—they exchanged words on a few occasions.

Several in our group tired of Peter's talking, leaving and moving on with their day; I remained, tirelessly listening to his stories and ideas and stray thoughts for however long he chose to stay. We have a few bits of food and much coffee—I paid for one round (€ 25,30) and Peter thanks me with a subtle nod of his head. He asks me about my research, interested in my thoughts on Marcel Duchamp, an artist that seemed of little interest to Peter; maybe he was simply interested in my interest. I only meet Peter three times after this.

Plate 4: Peter Porçal

Plate 5: A memorable dinner at Pepo

9 Correggio's Allegories for Isabelle d'Este of Mantua's Study [excerpt]

Erwin Panofsky once observed ironically that the academic industry known as art history wasn't exempt from a certain absurdity, that its similarity to Parkinson's laws wasn't by chance. One of these, as Panofsky says, is that the more research is carried out on the crux of an artwork, the more our understanding of it seems to diminish. Thus, if one art historian has written four pages on a certain problem, it takes his colleague sixteen pages to refute his paper, while a third will need sixty-four pages to re-establish the status quo. At this point it's worth saying that I really ought to bear this in mind, since I will spend about fifty pages to resolve this issue, when one of the most famous Frenchmen of the 1600s tried to deal with it not in four pages but in four lines.

The subject of this present study is to probe into the meaning of the two unparalleled paintings of allegorical subjects painted by Antonio Allegri, called Correggio, for Isabelle d'Este's study at Mantua. The interpretation of these two paintings is like the rule referred to by Panofsky in respect of the progressive diminution of our comprehension. As early as the middle of the 1600s, there is little doubt that in the two works Correggio wanted to paint the allegory of Virtue and Vice, and we can strengthen ourselves in that conviction following different interpretations right up to the most modern.

And yet, there is something that doesn't add up in the number of these attempts. The need for a new explanation of an allegory, at least one that we can believe, in general can't be born out of suspicion about the validity of previous theses. But examining what has been written on the two paintings, no one, without exception, will find any discord on the global theme, because everyone is in complete accord that the two paintings represent Virtue victorious over Vice. So then, what need is there to always be making new interpretations? The truth is, that there are in our painting's minor personifications, the identity and function of whom continue to escape explanation, and therefore even if we believe we have by now grasped the principle theme, one proceeds to discuss these minor figures. Such a paradox could never be made clearer than in the words of an art historian who recently wrote on Correggio, of which he said, "[he] searches for the sense of this complicated allegory, it results clearly enough as much based on how it concerns the general reference to Vice and Virtue, but the interpretation of a single figure appears to be more difficult and controversial."

One can ask: can we truly have certainty about the overall meaning when we have to realize that there are elements in these allegories whose meaning continues to evade us? Thus, to conclude, in the face of such uncertainty, today several studies don't even maintain anymore that the two Correggio canvases represent Virtue and Vice, but prefer to speak not of allegories but moral subjects, even adding darkly their doubt that anyone will ever be able to understand its original meaning. And so, after many attempts over the last three hundred years, invoking Panofsky's paradoxical law, Correggio's allegories have been relegated to that small group of works of art whose meaning continues to escape us.

10 Idea

And in imagining the perfect art historian I shall depict them as such a person as has perhaps never existed. For I do not ask who they were, but what is that quality which is superior to everything else, which not always and perhaps never shines out unremittingly in their analysis of a work of art but sometimes in some part, more frequently with some, more seldom perhaps with others.

But I do not believe that there is nothing in any genre as beautiful as that from which it was copied, we cannot perceive either with eyes or ears or any other sense, but we comprehend it with our mind and with our thoughts; thus we can imagine things more beautiful than Michelangelo's sculptures, which are the most beautiful we have seen in their medium, and those pictures which I have spoken about (the *Doni Tondo,* or those in the Sistine Chapel); and indeed that artist, when he produced his *David* or his *La Notte,* did not look at [*scil.* real] human beings whom he could imitate, but in his own mind there lived a sublime notion of beauty; this he believed, on this he fixed his attention, and according to its likeness he directed his art and hand.

As there is in the world of shapes and figures something perfect and sublime, imagined by way of imitation, so do we see the image of perfect eloquence in the mind and only seek to comprehend its copy with the eyes that read the page. Panofsky, that mighty mentor and teacher not only of art but also of historical perspective, calls these forms of things "ideas"; he quotes Cicero, in his *Orator,* who tells us of Plato who asserts that these "ideas" "exist eternally, being contained in our reason and our intellect: all else is born, remains in a state of flux,

29

glides down and does not long remain in one and the same state." Thus whatever is to be discussed with regards to the history of art must be located in relation to shared aesthetic forms and vision of that history.

II Forty

At a relatively young age the art historian had made the decision that reaching the age of forty would mark the end of their efforts to succeed publicly and of all their societal aspirations. The art historian was determined, once they reached this age and in whatever position they found themselves, no longer to struggle to deny their voice and their particular imaginings.

When the time came, while in the streets of Florence, the art historian had no trouble accepting this moment as the realization of a particular vision. Never being truly comfortable with the description "art historian," a designation attached to ways of practicing not practiced naturally by the art historian. Yet they came to accept such a title for one reason: commitment to art and its histories, not in label but as a mode of thinking. One practiced, idiosyncratically, as a series of encounters with histories and dialogues, with individuals and collectives, all related to tracing art's will.

Being an art historian is not a singular identity, but instead points towards a multitude of possible selves, some found, some borrowed, some created. On the old carousel located in the Piazza della Repubblica, in the evening after a memorable dinner at Pepo with friends that are loved ones, the art historian, sitting on a painted horse, paused at the age of forty to reflect on the question: *who am I?*

12 *Mental Habits*

As the young art historian walked, on one of those idle, quiet afternoons they knew so well how to spend, they happened to be on Via Ricasoli outside the Academia and decided to stop at La Feltrinelli bookstore across the street. After browsing a few minutes in the art section and picking up Panofsky's latest work, the young art historian noticed Peter Porçal sitting in the café area and went over to talk with him.

As Peter looked up he spoke, as if the two were in the midst of a conversation—*In contrast to a mere parallelism, the connection which I have in mind is a genuine cause-and-effect relation; but in contrast to an individual influence, this cause-and-effect relation comes about by diffusion rather than by direct impact. It comes about by the spreading of what may be called, for want of a better term, a mental habit—reducing this overworked cliché to its precise Scholastic sense as a "principle that regulates the act," principium importans ordinem ad actum. Such mental habits are at work in all and every civilization.*

13 Galileo's Telescopes

The art historian left their apartment at 10:45 on foot (rain). Arrived at Museo Galileo at 10:55. Purchased an entry ticket (€ 10,00) and promptly went up to view Galileo's telescopes. The room was empty for the most part, one nearby visitor standing alone for some time before walking into another gallery. The telescopes are presented in a display cabinet on a wall, both on an angle, the larger 1273 mm long telescope from around 1610 hung overtop the earlier 927 mm long telescope from around 1609.

Located in the bottom of this same display cabinet, along with several other items, is a copy of Galileo's 1610 book *Sidereus Nuncius* opened to a page showing two etchings of the rough and uneven moon. It was an image the art historian had spent much time with over the past seven years, from the time they first began researching the astronomer and his practice. Positioned with a good view of this case, of the telescopes, the art historian made a quick ink sketch in a blue marbled notebook, not seeking fidelity but rather thinking about the device through the act of drawing.

On a separate page, they made notes about an unrelated research project, an idea for which imposed itself on the art historian at this moment—if not recorded, many of such ideas vanish quickly. (Days later, when looking through this notebook, the art historian will add a note under the drawing that reads: *Although the camera obscura is traditionally recognized as the precedent for the photographic camera, I believe the telescope more properly anticipates the most celebrated qualities of photography.*) Left the Museo Galileo at 2:07 PM for an appointment at Il Torchio, arriving late at store of the Florentine bookbinder Erin Ciulla. Discussed the details of a book being produced and bound by Erin. Already having decided the specifics of the cover material and paper stock for the interior, this visit was dedicated to examining samples of endpapers, of which Erin, aware of the art historian's indecisiveness, pre-selected four samples of patterns and colourations.

Asked again if she had created each of these endpaper designs herself, she confirmed, proceeding to tell a brief technical story of the fabrication the marbled pages *(mostly emblem of my work!)*. Left Il Torchio at 3:20 after purchasing a small blue marbled notebook (€ 20,00) to be put into use immediately, as the previous small blue marbled notebook—slightly different, the old one had subtle additions of yellow whereas the new one was more *blue*—had just been filled that day.

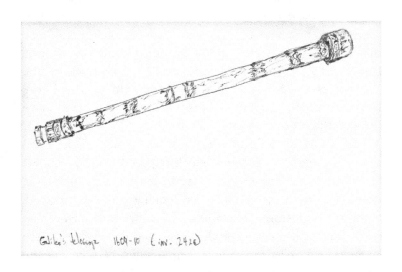

Plate 6: The art historian made a quick ink sketch

34

Plate 7: Il Torchio

Plate 8: Burian Bar

14 Closed

The art historian left their apartment at 11:00 on bicycle. Arrived at San Marco at 11:05 AM and found the premises to be closed. The list of hours indicates it is open on this day at this time, and no additional notices of closure apparent. The art historian accepted this moment of chance, going about their day unfazed. Left San Marco at 11:14, unsure of a precise destination. Passing the Burian Bar, a welcoming café located at the intersection of three roadways, the art historian stopped in for a coffee, sitting outside even though there was a chill in the air. The ideas of a recent Donatello exhibition at the Palazzo Strozzi weighed on their mind; the layers of perspectives in *Feast of Herad*. Lost track of time, leaving the café sometime in late afternoon. Arrived at their apartment, on bicycle, at 3:20 PM.

15 *Goethe*

On a shelf in my study there is a small bust of Johann Wolfgang von Goethe. All white, he is pictured from the shoulders up, head turned slightly to the right, a rather traditional rounded base makes it appear as a copy of an old bust. It was a fortieth birthday present from Miriam, who purchased it in the giftshop of the Berlin Altes Museum and presented it to me in the adjacent café. We had travelled to Berlin specifically to see the exhibition *On the Trails of the Iroquois* at Martin-Gropius-Bau, which also had on view a wonderful Meret Oppenheim Retrospective. After visiting Christian Boltanski's *The Missing House,* we made our way to the nearby museum island that includes the Altes Museum. While stopping for a coffee and small bite to eat, Miriam left quickly and returned with a small box; while it was still days until my actual birthday, she insisted that I open it—and Goethe was inside. Miriam and I shared a laugh at the fact that, as we were about to travel to Florence in just over a day's time, we would bring Goethe with us to Italy.

I would like to direct the attention of scholars towards a source of art historical understanding that until now has been neglected to the same degree that literary sources offering information about localization and chronology have been the object of the greatest appreciation and the most diligent study. To be sure, a generation that preferred to see the work of art as an accidental convergence of signs, borrowed meanings, and apparently ahistorical significations was incapable of thinking of the pronouncements of art historians on the *meaning* of their time as anything other than speculative fantasies. In the eyes of (so-called) post-modernists there can be no conscious *meaning,* and whatever was said about such *meaning* in modernist verse can only be, at best, worthless self-deception, if not deliberate deceit.

⁓⁖⁓

Once one recognizes that humanity wants to find and create interpretive phenomena presented in images and visions, encountered as ideas and concepts, always in different ways in different times, then one will embrace the notion that interpretations by thoughtful and well-informed individuals about meanings to be considered for a work of art experienced in their time deserve the full consideration of art historians. For what beckons us is a way of convincing ourselves that our views about potential artistic meanings in a given moment—based, necessarily, on subjective interpretations of an object as it exists or is created in this time—are in fact also the views of those who lived in times previous, maybe even in future times. In other words, whether in fact people expected from the visual arts that which, on the basis of research into the history of art, we imagined the "willed" to have been. This correspondence would clearly be the only true and reliable proof of the results of our research.

17 Everything Here is Wrong

The art historian left their apartment at 10:53 walking. Stopped for a coffee at Caffè Notte on Via delle Caldaie. Sitting at a small table in the back room, the art historian was preoccupied with a particularly insidious research problem. Weeks of obsessive consideration had obtained no tangible results, aside from frustration and concern regarding the viability of this particular avenue of thought. Almost immediately upon arriving, several books were removed from a brown leather side bag and arranged on the small café table—André Breton's 1928 Surrealist novel *Nadja,* opened to a page that shows a photograph of the *Humanité* bookstore; the first volume of Julia Cartwright's *Isabella D'Este Marchioness of Mantua 1474-1539,* closed but with a piece of paper, slightly larger in size than the book itself, tucked into its pages; a rather worn copy of *Under Blue Cup* by Rosalind Krauss, open but with pages face down on top of the larger Cartwright; a small dark green book, Federica Bosco's *L'artsista.*

Throughout their time at this table, the art historian would only consult one of these books: Breton's. The others remained undisturbed until they were again collected in preparation for leaving the café at 1:15 PM. Arrived at the Laurentian Library at 1:47. Standing for an extended duration in the vestibule, the art historian once again observed the various elements of Michelangelo's architectural design. They were a constant source of confusion. From a side bag the copy of *Nadja* was taken out briefly—to read its opening sentence, where Breton asks the question *Who am I?* Followed by the removal of Cartwright's volume, from which the art historian extracted the piece of paper placed within—a page from Janson's *History of*

Art, on which is reproduced a wonderful black and white photograph of the Laurentian Library's vestibule, picturing the staircase from a slight angle. The stairs were a curiosity, but so were many of the features of this space. Reading the only underlined words on the loose page, the art historian said aloud: *everything here is wrong.* Years later the art historian could not recall this particular incident, but I will never forget it.

18 *The Young Art Historian's Story*

The young art historian tells a story of Peter Porçal speaking with Michelangelo's *Bacchus.* The two met one afternoon in a gallery at The Bargello, in the company of many a student and observer. Words were exchanged in the spirit of curiosity and recognition, although one could sense an overall misalignment of perspectives. However misquoted or misremembered the incident may have been, it seems unmistakable that at one moment Peter was to tell everyone in attendance *to look at the bum, children.* Pointing towards the Bacchus' *natiche,* Peter made a gesture this writer is reluctant to put into words—not out of inappropriateness, per se, but rather for fear of further misunderstandings about the episode. It is natural to be hesitant when it comes to interpreting the non-verbal nuances shared between friends, if in fact we can characterize Peter and Bacchus as friends. Their relationship has been a long one, although not without its dramas. But while Bacchus has had to accept what must feel like centuries of judgments and various criticisms—beginning, it must be acknowledged, with a rather significant dismissal by one Raffaele Riario—Peter's insistence of publicly addressing his backside is difficult not to take personally.

The apparent bitterness witnessed by the young art historian, real or simply perceived, may be part of the reason for Bacchus not being in attendance of Peter's funeral in the Cappella degli Artisti in Santissima Annunziata, although I dare say no one recognized his absence. Nor has it been demonstrated, by proof or by argument, that this Bacchus was even aware that Peter had passed. All evidence suggests that, similar to Bacchus' relationship with Michelangelo, the two spent time together and then no more. The reader may ask, what is all this story about?—An art historian and an artwork, said the young art historian—and one of the best of its kind, I ever heard.

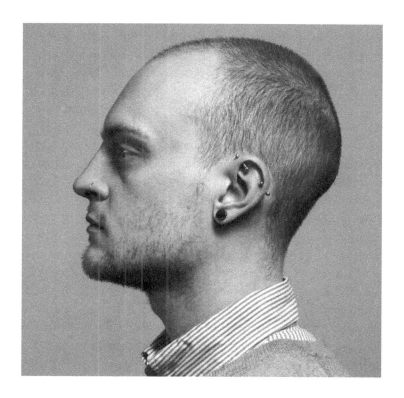

Plate 9: Maxwell Hyett

19 *Lecture on Galileo*

During my first visit to Florence I was invited to give a lecture to a class of students from OCAD University in Toronto, which was being taught by Andy Patton. I chose to talk about Galileo and the telescope, in part to encourage students to visit the nearby Galileo Museum, where his original telescopes are on view. While I honestly was uncertain how such a presentation would be received, I found it extremely satisfying to share my ideas about these famous telescopes within the same city that housed them. Miriam, Jamelie, Ron and I visited the Galileo Museum days before my lecture—I remember standing for some time with Jamelie in front of a large globe on display in one of the galleries.

While at the museum I took photographs of the telescopes on display, which I used in my talk to accentuate this sense of the topic's presence. As a way of considering how this optical device questioned ideas of vision, I discussed three ceiling paintings. The first, Michelangelo's *Sistine Chapel* ceiling, was created before the invention of the telescope. The second, Ludovico Cigoli's *Assumption of the Virgin* in Santa Maria Maggiore, created during Galileo's lifetime and with the astronomer's discoveries in mind. The third, Andrea Pozzo's *Glorification of Saint Ignatius* in the Church of Sant'Ignazio, was created in the aftermath of Galileo's telescopic discoveries and the changes in the very foundations of human experience that the device brought.

Following my lecture a young art historian, Maxwell Hyett, asked a compelling question about vision—(subsequently he kept in contact with me, becoming a close friend). The other significant encounter was with Peter Porçal, who attended my lecture. Following this talk, sitting at a small table in a nearby café, he wrote a list of places for me to visit in Florence for my research on Galileo.

The other conversation I recall, again related to my topic, was Peter Porçal's instructions on how to visit the churches I discuss, all of which are in Rome and relatively close to the train station—I would visit all three in a few years time. It was during my lecture, as part of the question period, that Peter Porçal shared with me some thoughts about his ideas on perspective and Michelangelo. This was the second of three meetings I would have with him. Peter Porçal was extremely generous with his knowledge, giving lengthy responses on both topics that are worth remembering in their entirety.

The problem of one-point perspective: there will always be that viewing point, which (as Julian mentioned) is for one person at once. I always say, *this is for me and then I will make space for her, and she will make space for...* etcetera, etcetera. Talking about space in architecture, for instance. It is not right now in our history a fashionable subject, no one is interested in space in architecture. It is very important and very simple, mainly there is between Renaissance and Baroque—such as Cigoli, Andrea Pozzo—in between Renaissance and Baroque there is Mannerism, which brought a certain (let us say) strange touch, and interrupts space so that it will not be so simple.

Do not think that Mannerism is simple. In the Renaissance, space in architecture is intelligible space, abstract space and deductive space—which means it is clearly defined. That is why Brunelleschi hated sculptures, he hated paintings but he hated especially frescos that open illusion into the sky. In his opinion, these illusionistic frescos destroy our perception of his proportions, harmony—1:2, 1:3, etcetera (he had many other more complex ratios, not that we can understand these ratios with the naked eye). Brunelleschi's universe should be intelligible, absolutely intelligible; he tries to create crystal clear sculpture, crystal clear structure, *crystal clear.* You are not supposed to be left doubting, *is it so,* instead you can say, *this is so high (va bene).* Mannerism brings to Brunelleschi's harmony a refinement—that which was in Brunelleschi is 1+1+1+1+1+1, it becomes in Mannerism 1+1:1, 1+1:1 (they put two columns, one next to another). Then we will get Baroque; in Baroque it is unintelligible space, we are not supposed to understand it that much—*unintelligible* space and indefinite space. In the Church of Saint Ignatius, they did not have the money to construct a dome. There was a Cardinal who said: *no, do not worry, you are Jesuits and I will leave money for construction of the dome;* when he died they opened his, let us say last will, there was not a cent for the dome. At this point Andrea Pozzo said: *do not worry I will fix it.* They closed the opening that was waiting for a little dome, covered the opening (the drum let us call it) with a huge painting on canvas, which represents one-point perspective practically but it works only up to a certain point. When we go there are points, little circles of a different coloured (yellow) marble, you have to stop here and here; then you stop at the last circle. This is the last moment when it still works. Once you pass over that one point, the last one, the yellow circle, finally you will discover this is total deceit. Only then do you realize that it is a painting, it is not a real dome. There are all these points and these points are always for one person at once. This is the problem: they pay respect to a single person. There is always one point, and unfortunately I have to give my one point to her so that she will have this perspective and she will have to pass it to another. In the Renaissance the subject is 'I'—Peter and then her, and her and her. In Baroque we will not have any more this sort of fixed point. Maybe Andrea Pozzo will be the last one who manipulates you; he knows exactly that the little trick of the painted dome does not work if you do not respect *his* mathematically defined points.

There is in Rome another similar place, Francesco Borromini's corridor at the Palazzo Spada. Borromini is a crazy man; when he died they would find in his home something like 10,000 books—can you image, in the 1660s (he committed suicide in 1667). Not only this, he collected shells. He had agents who would collect for him while they were on business shells, seashells; he would cut the shells in half and he would study the proportions inside the shells. A genius, a weird man, he would dress always in black and the only colour he would have are (something like) two carnations, done from cotton, attached to top of his shoes. Popes did not like to deal with him; in visitors' book in the Vatican 360 times has been received Bernini and Borromini 27 times, they just keep their nose closed and they are sure to send him off as soon as they can. (If you face a divorce committee, they will ask: *Peter, why do you want to divorce from your wife?* And I will say, *well, my wife loves Bernini and I love Borromini,* and they will say, *this is not a healthy marriage, you have to divorce."*)

Borromini created reverse perspective, at the Palazzo Spada, which means the walls of the corridor are converging so that the walls go up and the ceiling goes down. At the end there is an arch, behind that arch there is a former garden with a small sculpture. If I walk to the end of this corridor, at the end at that arch, which seems to be an enormous arch, I would hit with my head on the top of that arch; it is very, very small. This is also fooling the eye but again it calls for a certain (let us say) fixed point of view. It is reverse perspective but it is always perspective *(va bene).* In Baroque art there is not anymore one fixed point. Which is to say, it became art for the masses, for the public. The subject, it is us not me and her and her, like in the Renaissance—I have to make space for her and she has to make space for her. In the Baroque, (almost) whatever space you stay it is good, it is correct. The Renaissance: abstract, well defined, *intelligible* space. In the Baroque: unintelligible, indefinite and often indiscernible from a distance. If the dome at the Church of Saint Ignatius were well illuminated you would instantly see it was fake.

21   Peter's Second Response—Michelangelo

With Michelangelo's ceiling, the Sistine Chapel ceiling, you have to be careful with one thing. Michelangelo is not well educated of a man, he is not your Galileo. Michelangelo, he is living for a while in the Medici Palace here with the best *intellegencia* in Europe. The Medici's were collecting these *intellegencia;* philosophers, they had Giovanni Pico della Mirandola, there is Marsilio Ficino, Angelo Poliziano, there are musicians and etcetera, etcetera.

The fact that Michelangelo could have stayed and lived together in the same space, as indeed he were an adoptive child of the Medici family—four and a half years in this richest family in the world at that moment—with major *intellectia,* forced German art historians in the 19th century to over interpret Michelangelo. Right now we are in the moment when the Catholic Church, the Vatican produced several excellent art historians who deeply believed in, publishing books about Michelangelo the theologian. One of them lives here in Florence, Timothy Verdon, an American. The other one lives in Rome, he is a Cardinal and the head of the Pontifical Council for Culture—let's say the department of culture for the Church throughout the whole world—Gianfranco Ravasi. Yesterday I did buy two booklets they published on Caravaggio and on the image of god; this is all nonsense. They open Bible and book and its full of quotations, etcetera. Whatever you say, Michelangelo is not well educated. These Germans imposed on our reading of Michelangelo that he is an intellectual. (I have never met an art historian who has memorized all the names of all the protagonists painted on the Sistine Chapel ceiling, they are very obscure ancestors of Jesus Christ from

Jewish history.) Michelangelo does not speak Latin. The little bit of Classical mythology he has learned was from his friend—and this is a very delicate problem—Angelo Poliziano, who is the most brilliant mind in the city. It will be Poliziano who will interest Michelangelo a little bit in Classical mythology.

Who did design for Michelangelo the ceiling? There is not even a little piece of paper in which they will acknowledge him; his name was Piero Vaccaro. He was the brilliant mind in theology living with Michelangelo inside the Vatican when he was working on the ceiling. So it would make sense that Piero Vaccaro did the program. The program is quite complex, but not the central part. No, the central part is like a warning: we are fragile... we are a helpless race.

There are two main failures of the human race: Adam and Eve, and Noah—who did not do too much, he got drunk; he got nude, showing the offensive parts of his body to everyone, with his three sons, two are laughing at their father and the third one is trying to cover up the offending parts of his father's body. In both cases, God trusted them as much as he could hoping that he would get, after Adam and Eve, and especially after Noah, that he would get a *better* human race, better. But it did not work. Why? What is the message of the Sistine Chapel ceiling? We are a helpless race. We human race, although created by God, we always will fail. God can trust us as much as he wants but we always will fail. We need extra help. We need Jesus to come on Earth, God will send a redeemer, someone who will help us. So the whole Sistine Chapel ceiling it only talks about the terrible necessity of the coming of Jesus Christ on Earth who will help us and who will sort of straighten a little bit that curved piece of wood that we are—you know, the human race. All of the prophets and ancestors of Jesus Christ—and it is difficult to memorize their names—they are here to prove the deep roots of the Jesus Christ and that the necessity that the coming of Jesus Christ has been announced already, 700 years before he was born *(va bene)*. This is why it is so complex, so complicated. But you don't have to be scared when you look at that ceiling, the significance of that ceiling is very simple: we are a helpless race, we always will fail. What we need is that God will be so gentle and now send some messenger, somebody who will help us, since without his help (extra help), we will never be that what he wanted us to be.

This is so complex that Michelangelo could not have created this program. And this again is the debt of the Germans, the *overinterpretation* of Michelangelo. If you look at the *Prisoners* here, in the Accademia, they are slaves and they are prisoners. And I always say, prisoners of what war, what war was it that they were taken prisoner, they were taken into captivity? You have to look for one common denominator, among these sculptures, and you will find very simply that they are touching their heads with their hands. It stands for sleep or death. We have lost that knowledge, so we have to study it. These four guys, which are differently interpreted—it is published and over-published—they are labeled captives and prisoners and slaves, especially *slaves* (they call one of them *awakening slave*). These are all Romantic 19th century categories and labels. You have to look with fresh eyes; all four have something in common, they are all touching their heads, so they have something to do with *sleep or death.* Go to Michelangelo's own *Life,* he published in 1553—only it was written by Ascanio Codivi; it would be too crazy, even for Michelangelo, that he would say 'Michelangelo Buonarroti, my own life' or 'how I did it'. He paid a guy who became his friend, a writer, and he would write it from his own view. But everyone knows that Michelangelo paid him, sitting next to him saying 'no, no, this you do not publish,' dictating his own life. On page 26 you will run into these four guys from the Galleria dell'Accademia. He says only a few words about them, saying that they are imprisoned in death. They are all imprisoned in death, which is why they are touching their heads in their hands.

So we have to be very careful today, these studies, one life is not enough to read everything that has been published until now about Michelangelo. You will waste your whole life to read every article and every book. And I think the end of your life would be a disaster, you would be completely confused; you have to be highly selective. But one thing you have to keep in mind, once and forever, is that he is not an intellectual. Michelangelo is *not* an intellectual. He is not your Galileo.

22 Art's Will

All of art history presents itself as a continuous struggle with
material; it is not the tool—which is determined by the technique—but the idea that strives to expand its creative realm
and increase its formal potential. Such will is central to the
creative act, not just the means of artistic creation that is the
direct consequence of technique, but the idea or conception
initiated by the artist and completed by a viewer. Art history
is the crossroads of this ideation, a moment—atemporal by the
nature of its quest—in which the will of an artwork, more than
the artist or a viewer, becomes conscious. It is the work of art
that is the will driving acts of human creation.

23 *Morning*

The art historian stepped outside their apartment building at 8:50 AM. Standing in the morning sun, admiring the day as it starts on this narrow street, a door in the next building over opened and a man stepped out around 8:53. The two acknowledged each other's presence with a subtle nod of the head. The art historian had not met the man before this moment but knew him to be the Russian filmmaker Andrei Tarkovsky. The two stood parallel, almost unmoving, each in front of their respective doorway, for an undetermined amount of time. Around them: tens, hundreds of simultaneous actions, micro-events, each one of which necessitates postures, movements, specific expenditures of energy. All the while the two remained relatively still. Perhaps coincidentally, the filmmaker turned and stepped back into his apartment building at the precise moment a women passed by, across the road, walking her long-haired standard dachshund. Not too long afterwards the art historian retreated as well.

Plate 10: On this narrow street

24 Tarkovsky in Florence

In 1985 Andrei Tarkovsky moved into his apartment at 91 Via San Niccolo, located on the sixth floor of an old building in the Oltrarno. His wife Larisa—assistant director on a number of his films—arrived ahead of time to furnish the 120 square meter flat, which, as we are told, was given to them by the mayor of Florence. While in Berlin Larisa bought lots of antiques for the apartment: plates, kitchen furniture, carpets, gorgeous old chandeliers and lamps, mirrors, candle holders. All necessary for a nice and homely place. She had to carry everything up to the sixth floor (no lift in the building, just a spiral staircase). And she secured the room on the higher floor for Tarkovsky's study. He had developed a special bond with Italy, as seen in his 1983 film *Nostalghia,* set in Tuscany's Bagno Vignoni. This location reflected qualities of Russia that, as an exile, he could no longer have—this made him feel at home and miss home at the same time. In the Uffizi he visited Leonardo da Vinci's *The Adoration of the Magi;* on one occasion he and Larissa were able to view the work when no public was in the museum, an intimate encounter with Leonardo.

Even when in Rome, after seeing the Sistine Chapel, there was something in Leonardo's work Tarkovsky found particularly captivating, a complexity maybe, or just a sense of how the artist saw the world; in conversation he discussed his admiration of Leonardo with fellow filmmaker Michelangelo Antonioni, who of course sided instead with Michelangelo's Sistine Chapel. At the time of moving into his apartment in Florence, Tarkovsky was in the process of editing his 1986 film *The Sacrifice,* which was to be his last. His health was poor, but he took solace in the fact that, after five years of misery, he and Larissa had their own home. In November he has a full month in Florence editing the film, everyday, as he said, from 9:00 AM to 7:00 PM.

I imagine him on some mornings, stepping out of his building, standing in the narrow street, just to admire the day. I imagine him in his study, which is miraculously arranged in a manner that reflected his Russian sensibilities—with whitewashed walls, the room filled with the infinite lives of the objects within it: fresh flowers in a simple glass vase, photographs on the walls, lithographs and reproductions of varying sizes and in varying states of wear, on shelves among books, a library of research and pleasure, and all available surfaces filled with random things, almost always arranged into symmetrical groupings, a trace of existence in time.

25 The Study

They have been renovating the art historian's study. That delightful, tumble-down old space has lost its aged appearance as the high whitewashed walls, especially those opposite the desk, have been given some much needed attention. The many objects and things found around the room have been re-orchestrated: damaged objects removed, arrangements re-arranged, new things added and some that no longer speak within this space are put away.

One of several interesting additions is a small glass bush yam wrapped in white twine contained within a miniature coffin; one of four that were made by the Aboriginal Australian artist Yhonnie Scarce—it sits on a mid-level shelf of the bookcase by the study's door. Two selves above, closer to one end, is where in the near future a small bust of Goethe, bought for the art historian in Berlin, will be placed. A book lay in this old bookcase, of which the art historian cared to remember one picture—a man sitting, with legs crossed, seen from behind, on an angle, resting on a wooden Brancusi sculpture, waiting with a simplicity which touched the art historian strangely, an ambiguous care—*Marcel Duchamp,* not quite posing for a portrait—we all remember the art historian's convoluted story of acquiring this photograph while in Rome.

Photographs and small prints in the art historian's apartment that had been propped up on the bookshelves were removed, dusted and some put back, while others were placed randomly inside various books (presumably to be flattened). Books were removed in areas under renovation, piled on the floor near the desk. The few paintings found in the study were taken out of the space for the duration of this process, all but one that the art historian could not do without. This *Portrait of a Study* was painted specifically for the art historian, a mirror reflection on this world that is their study which exists as an infinite reconstitution of its own knowledge. As for the slight variations from one arrangement of the study to another—spatial, and at the same time temporal, layers of perspectives imagined in and through the representation of this space—which had so exacerbated the visitors' curiosity, they could well be the ultimate expression of the art historian's effectual truth: as though, while composing the material history of his own historicization through the history of other art historians, they had momentarily been able to make a presence of encountering the constellations of existing historical orders, thus reaching a creativeness beyond enunciation, a flash of inspiration beyond citation and a will beyond memory.

It is common that at these moments the art historian finds wayward items—those that have fallen behind a row of books or to the back of a bookshelf, those placed inside books and been forgotten, those books that by chance have been shelved in a random location and can now be returned to the existing orders. But not this time. A copy of *Esposizione di Pittura Futurista di "Lacerba"* that the art historian had been looking for for nineteen months, which was in fact misplaced within the study, remained unfound.

26 In the Presence of Schopenhauer

New Years in Florence. Miriam found an apartment that had been part of the palazzo where 19th century German philosopher Arthur Schopenhauer lived when in Florence. A magnificent space located on Borgo Pinti, we were stunned as we walked in, especially seeing the high frescoed ceilings in the living room. Sitting under this ceiling, on an old overstuffed couch (beige with brown trim), I read from Schopenhauer's *Essays and Aphorisms: This will, as thing in itself, is known to us only in and through the act of volition, and we are therefore incapable of saying or of conceiving what it is or does further after it has ceased to perform this act: thus this denial of the will to live is for us, who are phenomena of volition, a transition to nothingness.* Reading these words, looking up at the frescos on the ceiling painted in the 18th century, I imagine Schopenhauer looking up at these same images in the same general space. I could really feel his presence. Our lives unfold in space, and time is just an inessential left-over.

While I have an unnecessarily precise memory of the places where the events of my life have occurred, I can locate these events in time only as a series of contrived and approximate overlaps. So when I read these words from *Essays and Aphorisms* in this possibly shared space with its author, I may have been aged forty-four, but equally possibly forty, or forty-seven. That evening, under the same frescos Schopenhauer once observed, Miriam and I celebrated New Year's Eve with Italian potato chips, soda and prosecco, watching the films *Blade Runner* and *Blade Runner 2049* back-to-back. An amazing way to bring in the New Year.

Plate 11: Seeing the high frescoed ceilings

27 Two Lights

It was a winter-scene, by Sophie de Niederhäusern and/or by Marcel Duchamp. All the delicate poetry together with all the delicate comfort of a frosty season was in the leafless branches turned to silver, the soft foliage bordering a small body of water, the undefined edges framing an imagined encounter, the gleams of bright dabs of colour, one red, one yellow or green, resting on the surface of a reproduced image as if witnessing from the window of a train two lights receding into a distant landscape. The art historian, caught in a moment of distracted reverie, gazed into the dark of a dual illumination with the red and yellow-green theoretical lights; for the vision of the art historian dwelt much on the sheer coincidence of colour, at once lost in the past, as one experiences the act of seeing a portrait in the mind, and imitating the present in the gesture of capturing lights without the possibility of a singular reality.

"Of course the real art historian bore not the faintest resemblance to the imaginary portrait I have sketched"... "Many times I took up my pen and many times I laid it down again, not knowing what to write"... "Then I began to weep very piteously; and not only in my imagination but with my eyes, which were wet with tears"... "I know there's an empty place near here, exhausted by the art historian's imaginary encounters"...

29   Notes Concerning the Chance Encounter of Books

I had been talking about this a few days before with the art historian when a lovely winter day in 2017 invited us to stroll near Mercato di Sant'Ambrogio. The objects that, between the lassitude of some and the desire of others, go off to dream at this outdoor market had been just barely distinguishable from each other in the first hour of our stroll. They flowed by, without accident, nourishing the meditation that this place arouses, like no other, concerning no precarious fate of so many little constructions.

The first ones to attract me were a particular grouping of four books at one of the small bookstalls. An older woman, immersed in a newspaper, sits looking overtop two tables completely covered with a random assortment of aged books, some appearing lightly abused by whatever history proceeded this moment, others having lost this battle with time rest in virtual tatters. Within the disordered ordering, trapped amongst a visible series of Italian literary classics and what I assume to be popular fiction from the 1930s, four unique volumes find themselves together as an island of visual distinction. All oriented the same way, different from all those around, I lean in to inspect this intriguing constellation. On the left, brown leather with gold lettering on the spine, Elizabeth Daniel's sensation novel *Miriam's Sorrow* published in 1863; originally a two-volume publication, this version is a custom hardcover binding with both volumes in one book. Immediately to the right, red card cover with title and author in black text, a 1973 English edition of *Don Quixote* by Miguel de Cervantes; this cheap mass paperback is well used, with a rather whimsical note written on the inside of the back cover that reads: *I thought of the walls as pages from a giant book, with its spine in the Arno River and its pages open toward the city.* Between this last title and the final is a rather sad Italian paperback copy of Dante Alighieri's *La Vita Nuova;* missing its front cover, the spine peeling off to reveal the glued pages, I honestly am not even sure why this particular book is available for purchase. The group ends with a small 2010 English version of Roberto Bolaño's *Antwerp;* a beautiful hardcover book, nicely designed and in good condition, it made the tattered book to its left more visually interesting.

The remarkably curious character of these four volumes— two hardcovers framing two paperbacks—did not escape the eye of the art historian, who recognized in their chance meeting on this table a potentially *catalyzing* moment of perception pointing towards the need to observe how life outside us develops apart from our assumed sense of singular identities. Insisting I purchase the entire grouping, the art historian had already selected a location for their placement—always together—within my study. While unable to be convinced to acquire the lot, I could not stop my admiration for the small Bolaño hardcover that felt nice in my hands. I bought the book (€ 28,00) and carried it off immediately.

Plate 12: Parva Libreria

30 Sleep or Death

The art historian left their apartment at 10:50 AM. Quick conversation with an old friend near Borgo Pinti before continuing on to get coffee at L'Osteria Dell'Ok. The café was empty. Selecting a small table to the side, closest one of the windows facing Via Dei Servi, the art historian took out a small blue marbled notebook and wrote down a thought—*you have to look with fresh eyes. All four of Michelangelo's Prisoners have something in common, they are all touching their heads.*

This is related to the idea of sleep or death. This last concept had been on the art historian's mind for some time. Years before Peter Porçal had spoken about this idea, convinced it was important to Michelangelo's understanding of his *Prisoners.* Originally intended to be part of a large funerary monument, these figures, partially visible, partially contained in the stone, appear to be struggling to escape their prison of marble. Holding their heads in their hands, each appears to be confronting the question of life and death.

The art historian left the café, walked down Via degli Alfani, stopping to purchase a catalogue on Lucio Fontana (€ 15) seen in the window of Parva Libreria, eventually arriving at the Accademia at 12:21 PM. It was closed that day but a person was waiting to allow entry, following the art historian as they walked directly into the room that housed the Prisoners. The two spoke briefly, as friends. Once alone, the art historian began to make sketches of the sculptures, drawing details of the moments when form turned to rock—*Auguste Rodin did this in the 19th century, but how could Michelangelo conceive of this in the Renaissance?* Notes of random thoughts were made alongside images, both tracking observations on and around the experience. (One of the more arbitrary notes was the beginning of an imaginary letter to Socrates by Petrarca: *I am going to tell you about last night's dream.*) These prisoners definitely speak of death, but what they might say about sleep fascinated the art historian, especially when considered in relation to Petrarca's words. To think about the role of sleep in the *Prisoners,* holding their heads in their hands—these partial figures question inner consciousness by never quite being allowed to exist.

31 Cavalcanti

As Peter Porçal walked, one quiet afternoon, he directed his friend Dr. Andrew Patton in the direction of the IBS Bookstore on the Piazza del Duomo. The two had been sharing a coffee and conversation nearby when, in a moment of confession, Dr. Patton admitted never having read the Italian poet Guido Cavalcanti. The profound silence that followed was broken when Peter Porçal forcibly escorted Dr. Patton to the nearest bookstore, marched him to the order desk and, speaking Italian, instructed the clerk to order him a book of Cavalcanti's verse in Italian and English. The woman, in the overtly calm demeanor typical of a bookstore clerk, showed Dr. Patton on a computer screen the complete bilingual edition of Cavalcanti (€ 120,00). Dr. Patton hesitated, not wanting to insult Peter Porçal, but demonstrating his reluctance regarding the commitment of this particular edition. Recognizing this reticence, the clerk offered an additional option, this one a more modest paperback edition that bore the simple title *Complete Poems* (€ 14,30). Agreement was reached, the book was ordered and Dr. Patton could see a renewed calm on the face of Peter Porçal.

32   *I Remember Peter*

I first met Peter Porçal in a small café in Florence. We spoke for several hours, with him telling me numerous stories. I remember the way he told the stories, often quite emphatic, very much directed at his listener. I remember the details he went into, which were fruitful for the imagination. I remember Peter talking about his visits to the office of the famed art historian Horst Waldemar Janson, telling me of several encounters. I remember Peter describing, often with some humorous impressions, how Janson looked wearing large gold chains and his long face, which was why he was called *the horse*. I remember Peter's voice, the way it deepened when he said, repeatedly, "the horse."

I remember Peter talking about meeting Erwin Panofsky, whose understandings of art and life he admired greatly. I remember Peter recounting an incident in which Panofsky was given an award by the German government, which he turned down, reminding everyone that as a German Jew he was forced to escape Germany during the Holocaust and live in exile. I remember Peter's immense respect for this fellow art historian. I remember Peter talking with me about Galileo, after my lecture. I remember Peter writing a list of sites related to Galileo that he felt I should visit for my research, with wonderful instructions. I remember hearing about Andrei Tarkovsky, who lived in the apartment building next to Peter's in the Oltrarno. I remember Peter noting that, on more than one occasion, he exchanged words with the filmmaker.

I remember Peter being excited to talk about the film *Nostalghia,* which Tarkovsky set in Bagno Vignoni—Peter described to me a particularly moving scene but I forget the specifics. I remember Peter's characterization of Tarkovsky as depressive, the manner in which he spoke and his general demeanor, yet he seemed to understand the world. I remember Peter's way of remembering Tarkovsky. I remember Peter's way of remembering. I remember Peter sitting very still, looking out from the café, very contemplative. I remember Peter sitting very still.

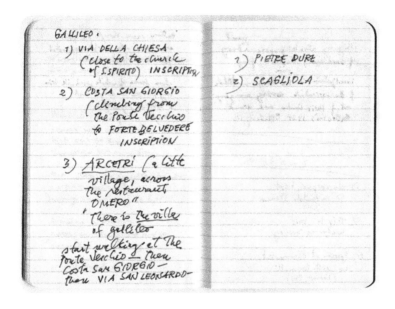

Plate 13: I remember Peter writing a list of sites related to Galileo

Plate 14: San Marco

33 San Marco

The art historian left their apartment at 10:48 on bicycle and arrived at San Marco at 10:57. Purchased a ticket (€ 4,00 but only asked to pay € 3,00). A possible project had been preoccupying the art historian, on Fra Angelico's fresco the *Mocking of Christ*. This image had always seemed quite surreal and today was the first opportunity to sit in front of the work and consider this perspective. Upon entering the art historian paused in the courtyard, on the way to the stair leading up to the monk's cells. A different idea took hold and needed to be materialized. Removing a pen, blue marbled notebook and a paperback copy of Niccolò Machiavelli's *Il Principe* from a side bag, the art historian prepared to capture this idea before it vanished. But as usual it was resistant, always only partially visible. The pen almost touches the paper, is raised and subsequently lowered and almost touches again. Such a pattern repeated, with only rare moments of contact. Even then hardly a sentence was completed without a word crossed out, or an arrow drawn adding layers of attempts to make real—it is the mess of thoughts actually functioning. During this timeless period the art historian sat, alternating between writing and looking off aimlessly into space. People passed without notice.

This encounter with an idea took over the focus on the visit, which eventually succumbed to the necessities of this inner world. Even after making it upstairs, the art historian wandered almost aimlessly, remembering the intended purpose on the visit only after laying eyes on the floating body parts of the *Mocking of Christ*. But distraction triumphed and the possibility of a future project was put off for another visit—as it happened, in a few days time.

34 Astrologia

Seated in the lower right corner of Correggio's *The Allegory of Virtue,* prominently beside the central figure of Minerva, Astrologia looks out at the imaginary viewer. To understand exactly the reason why Correggio had included her next to the triumphant Minerva and the Four Virtues is not easy. Only in the most recent interpretations can one glimpse attempts to explain the possible logical connection: to indicate Astrologia in this personification and to speak of the most elevated sciences, the science of the heavens, means to effectively identify in itself an art, a very precise discipline, developed together with mathematics and medicine and taught during the 1400s and 1500s in studies of astrology. If occasionally several interpretations of our painting hint at a determinist essence to this art (... the destiny of a man is determined by the stars... Peter Porçal) it is not clear in what way this astral determinism could enter into a system of ethics, with the Four Virtues and the Triumph of Minerva, and this probably is because there is a will that is hidden in Astrologia.

35 Michelangelo's Will

During one of my encounters with Peter Porçal he shared his ideas on Michelangelo's Sistine Chapel ceiling. I had talked about this work in a recent lecture that he attended and, as it turned out, he had some interesting interpretations of the central scene of God and Adam. *They are touching fingers, but not for God to give Adam life, as the art historians often interpret this gesture. No, they call it "The Creation of Adam" but Adam clearly already has life, God reaching out with his finger is something more. We see Adam slumped over, lounging, with no torsion in his body. Michelangelo's figures, from his early Battle of the Centaurs, which he makes based on the suggestion by Poliziano, are defined through the power of the contortion of their bodies. But Adam here has none, which for Michelangelo is to have no will.* God is touching fingers to bestow Adam with *will.*

Peter's interpretation is undeniable for anyone who appreciates Michelangelo's art, his vision of humanity. The outward appearance of this contact, the iconic finger touching finger, attempts to capture an immaterial connection between individual and belief, between the self and the world of spirituality—the Renaissance used art to imagine this unimaginable encounter. Michelangelo truly believed his art was just such an expression, a deep *will* that is manifest visually in the bodily torsions that define his practice. When we witness the listless body of Adam, barely able to hold himself up, his arm resting on his knee and hand slumped over with only the slightest attempt to raise his index finger, it contrasts with the dramatic extension God's body, his legs crosses, beard blowing dynamically in the motion of the figure whose arm projects forward with a clear sense of determination focusing on his outstretched finger. God is granting Adam *will*—a human will that, through Humanism, is recognized as necessary if the idea of the human is to be re-born. And Michelangelo, whose art is an expression of such a human will, uses art's will to express his own unique vision of belief that is manifest in the contortions of the bodies he depicts.

What humanity needs is for God to give us will or the human cannot be what he wanted it to be. This is so complex that Michelangelo evidently took guidance from the Humanist scholars he was in contact with, notably Poliziano, but the precise envisioning of these ideas is palpably Michelangelo's. The material manifestation of human will, given by God to Adam in the literal touching of fingers, is a more appropriate interpretation of this famous encounter that is the centre of the world created on the Sistine Chapel ceiling. There is a tension throughout the ceiling's narrative between will and lack of will. Consider the drunkenness of Noah who is shown stripped of will, reflected in his acts of exposing himself, his sons trying to lessen his shame; like Adam, his body does not have the will to hold itself up properly. Such figures act as foils that accentuate the inner power of the human that Michelangelo continually champions, with *will* as the ideal essence of defining the interior world of modern subjectivity.

36 Palazzo Vecchietti

It is November, and a beautiful room for our first visit to Florence. A treat that Miriam arranged for my fortieth birthday. There is a small kitchen to the left as you enter, to the right a small hallway leading to the spacious bedroom that includes a nice table—where I sit writing these words. I would meet Peter Porçal in two days' time, but for now I imagine my life in this room, with its white trim and numerous drawings. Real drawings of nude figures and of architectural details, framed between glass with the wall visible beyond the outer limits of each sheet of paper.

I always travel with books, three on average, and this trip was no exception. A small stack on the table in front of me, I forget which books I decided to bring with me. I remember bringing the first volume of Poliziano's *Letters*—*I am sure that herein lies a failure, not so much of judgment as of will*—but this is for a trip to Rome that would not occur for several years. I remember bringing Hannah Arendt's *Love and Saint Augustine*—*in order to be, a person has to overcome their human existence, which is temporality*—however, I have been assured that I did no such thing. I remember bringing Kuo Hsi's *An Essay on Landscape Painting*—*the artist's fault is that of not putting their whole soul into their work*—yet this small volume was left with Erin Ciulla at Il Torchio for a project I would start in nine years. There is something about real pencil lines that is always lost in reproductions.

Often my choice of books depends on the specific projects I am working on at that moment. Which leads me to suspect that *The French Enlightenment and the Emergence of Modern Cynicism* by Sharon Stanley might have been one of the books

I have with me. Honestly, I do not remember—I can of course look over and see what is there, on the table, but I do not. Even though it is late, I am making myself a coffee just so that I can take advantage of what is a wonderful little kitchen. A common way for me to select books for a trip is to bring titles that relate to where I am going (sympathetic locality). It therefore makes sense that I would bring books like Galileo's *Sidereal Messenger* or Alberti's *On Painting*. I remember bringing Arthur Schopenhauer's *Essays and Aphorisms—the art of not reading is a very important one*—but this again is the memory of a future visit. I brought this to read because we stayed in the palazzo where Schopenhauer lived when in Florence. I remember underlining in that book, pencil lines beneath printed words. In the room the light is fairly dim, as I prefer it, just enough to be able to read and write. The shadows cast by the framed drawings are quite wonderful in the simple repetitions of forms, lines that are cast from the various light sources (stuttering). All three books are likely small, since I did not want to carry heavy books. I remember one having a textured white cover, because it visually reminded me of the white molding around the room, a dominant feature of the space. I remember the windows looking over a narrow street onto a building with beautiful, patterned tiles; Miriam took photographs of these tiles on our first night.

Thinking of the books I own with a white cover, the first one that comes to mind is Louis Althusser's *Machiavelli and Us,* but again I would not purchase this particular text until after my first visit to the Campidoglio in Rome, designed by Michelangelo—there is a reason for this connection that I will save for another time and story. On this particular evening I woke up in the middle of the night, walked down the small hallway to the small kitchen wearing the brown slippers provided by the hotel. It is nice to have this little kitchen, no matter how little use we have for it. Or maybe I brought *Moonwalking with Einstein* by Joshua Foer—no, this is one of the books the young art historian took with them on their trip to Florence. Standing in the little kitchen, in the middle of the night, I am thinking about the reality of being in here, in this city. Miriam is asleep. I know for a fact that I did not bring Hans Blumenberg's *The Genesis of the Copernican World*. I remember wanting to bring this book, which I was in the middle of reading, but it was too large (684 pages) and would take up too much space. I remember regretting this decision as I never finished reading the book. I would for sure bring *Three* by Perec—*for the artist has put their painting in the painting*—on one of my trips to Florence, but not this one; it would be the same visit that I purchased from La Libreria Alfani the Edizioni Henry Beyle printing of Georges Perec's *Sui diversi modi di usare il verbo abitare* (€ 18,00). One drawing of a reclining nude, mostly defined through line, is on a piece of paper that has sharp edges. As I look at it I cannot help but think it would have been more interesting, especially framed between two pieces of glass, if the edges of the paper were less defined.

I remember these floating worlds as a strong feature of the room's experience. I remember one book that I definitely brought with me, which had a detail of Benozzo Gozzoli's *Adoration of the Magi* on its cover. I did not yet know that Gozzoli apprenticed with Fra Angelico, assisting with the frescos in the monks' cells in San Marco. The room is quiet and Miriam is asleep. I walk down the small hallway towards the small kitchen.

37 The Study

The art historian returned to their apartment at 7:51 PM and goes right into their study. At the door they take off their clothes of the day, covered with visible soilings of the city, and put on their regal and scholarly garments; and decently reclothed, they enter the historical arena of art's history, where, received lovingly, the art historian feeds on the food that alone is theirs and they are born for. There the art historian is not ashamed to speak with art's history and to ask the reasons for its judgments; and art's history in its humanity replies to the art historian, and for the space of four hours the art historian feels no boredom, forgets every pain. They do not fear poverty, death does not frighten them. They deliver themselves entirely to art's history. And because Dante says that to have understood without retaining does not make knowledge, the art historian has noted what capital they have made from this conversation and have composed a little work *Imaginary Portrait of an Art Historian,* where they imagine as speculatively as possible into reflections on this subject, debating what art history is, of what kinds there are, how these histories are acquired, how they are maintained, why they are lost. And if you have ever been pleased by any of the art historian's whimsies, this one should not displease you; and to a young art historian, and especially a curious art historian, it should be welcome. Maxwell Hyett has seen it; he can give you an account in part both of the thing in itself and of the discussion he had with the art historian, although they are all the time fattening and polishing it.

The art historian left their apartment at 10:48 on foot (rain was expected) and arrived at the Uffizi around 10:57 AM. It is close to Christmas and the museum is closed. The art historian knocks on the door and is let in with a friendly greeting. Walking slowing through the uninhabited space, they make their way to the second floor. Into a gallery containing Giotto's *Virgin and Child* (Inventory 1890 no. 8344)—this was the last place the art historian laid eyes on Peter Porçal, who was engrossed with the teaching of students. *Giotto's great contribution was to introduce accidental and momentary qualities into figures' gestural language and, at the same time, allowing for the narrative depiction of current events.* The fact that Giotto and Dante were contemporaries, that they knew each other, always fascinated the art historian. Because both imagine an inner world of the human, an early modern sense of contained self.

After a given duration—short or long it is hard to say—the art historian proceeds, past several galleries. Standing quite close to Michelangelo's *Doni Tondo* (Inventory 1890 no. 1456), it is evident that the brush strokes on this round canvas tell a story. There is clover growing in the foreground of the scene, in front of the blue and pink fabric that Mary wears on her contorted body—that dynamically twists as she reaches around to grab baby Jesus. In her lap is a closed book. Interestingly, this painting makes an appearance in the film *Blade Runner 2049;* partially seen among a series of paintings, leaning against a large bookcase, it is contained within the rectilinear frame that it had been housed in during the 18th century (before being returned to its original round frame); all that is visible are the upper body and head of the child and the head, from the nose up, of St. Joseph. Before leaving the presence of this work, the art historian wrote a single word in Latin, limbus. Again past several galleries, until Leonardo da Vinci's *Adoration of the Magi* (Inventory 1890 n. 1594) presents itself, in its incompleteness. Why is the architectural structure in the background broken?

Looking at the many unfinished details, the art historian removed a book from a side bag, Andrei Tarkovsky's *Diaries*. Opening the volume to a pre-marked page, an entry from January 1985, the art historian read the following text (out loud or in their head I am unsure): *I spent several magnificent days in Florence with Lara. We went to the Uffizi Gallery at the time no public was there. The Adoration of the Kings is overwhelming* [...]. What was it about this painting that the filmmaker enjoyed so much?

Plate 15: The Uffizi and the Galileo Museum

39 *Draft of the Missing Thirty-Nineth Fragment*

Dust jacket: Appears to have been taken from the 1894 edition, *An Imaginary Portrait:* Spine size is slightly smaller than the 1887 first true edition hardback and the card inserted in the volume, also from the 1894 edition, includes an advert for Alois Riegl's Stilfragen (first published in 1893.) Light creasing and a few spots of foxing, otherwise excellent. Preserved in a removable jacket protector. Overall jacket condition is Very Good. Book cover: Bound by Alice Pattinson stamp-signed "AP" on rear turn-ins. Blue morocco binding with slight wear to ends of spine and corners of boards, a little rubbing to board edges.

An early example of Alice Pattinson's fine work. Alice Pattinson was one of a small group of distinguished female binders at work in England at the turn of the century. Among other distinctions, she was chosen (along with Katharine Adams and Florence Paget) as one of the three women employed to bind the forty copies of the Ashendene *Song of Songs* (1902), the illuminated book printed on vellum that stands as one of the greatest achievements of the modern private press movement. *Alice Pattinson set up her bindery in the rooms at 29 Gilbert Street in 1902. She received a good deal of praise for her bindings, which were illustrated in Art Workers Quarterly, Art Journal, and The Art of the Book (1914). Her work was indeed to a very high standard. Her bindings are signed with the monogram of her initials, similar to that of Annie Power, and are usually dated. She often showed her work at the Arts & Crafts Exhibition Society exhibitions, and also exhibited at Frankfurt in 1906, and at Leipzig in 1914.* Overall book cover condition is Good. Book interior: Complete volume, including 8pp blank at the back, after 4pp adverts. Heavy foxing to blue marbled endpapers, title page, all image pages and facing pages are foxed, patches of foxing to text. Inscribed by the author on the half-title page: "To Walter Pater in memory of a pleasant encounter. Nov: '14." Manuscript also includes small amount of marginalia in light pencil, two are quotations: the first on the verso of half title, reading: *The need to put on the blank page something I felt to be urgent without having the strength to do it completely, and the second on pp [73]: The world this (imaginary) art historian sets before us so engagingly has its care for the will, its volitionary preferences, in what one is to see—in the interiority of things—and there is something, a sign, a memento, at the least, of what makes art really valuable, even in that.* Overall book interior condition is Good Plus. Subject matter: Forty art historical and philosophical fragments set in Florence. Features the idea of imaginary encounters; encounters among personages of the figures of an "art historian" and the oxymoronic qualities of a world that resides in the juxtaposition of the cerebral and the material, the unreal and the real. Explores the development of its protagonist's multi-faceted existence, the art historian, navigating different encounters that problematize the referentiality of portraiture. Please Note: This item comes with its own one-book bookcase. Book size: 6.25 x 9 inches (15.5 x 22.5 cm). Hardback. Printed pages: 100.

40 Peter's Death

Our comparable Peter Porçal is no more! The art historian returned unexpectedly. I heard then hasty footsteps on the stairs. We turned together into the study; and the art historian told the story there. Peter departed suddenly, early 28 March 2014 after being rushed to the hospital by his daughter Cecilia, on one of those mornings that could have been described in the verses of Dante. At the last moment Peter had been at work upon a particular analysis of Michelangelo—*it is not life that God gives Adam, with the touching of fingers, rather he is given will. See the limpness of Adam's body, as if he possesses no will, no will to act in or on the world. This need for will as a cornerstone of belief is clear throughout Michelangelo's vision of art, his figures always struggle, against themselves, against their own existence.* Written in a small blue marbled notebook, these words reflect Peter's own belief in art's will, which acted upon his life. And the art historian never forgot this lesson. At the last moment Peter had been at work upon such a study of Michelangelo, liking little the prevalent studies currently celebrated. Peter died within all the sentiment of art's will. He had been ill for some time, needing often an oxygen tank to order to breath properly. He was always a seeker after something in the world that is therein no satisfying measure, or not at all.

Notes

The following are a series of major references that are made in this book, some presented directly and others I have altered to varying degrees. Note that minor references have not been cited and are either to be discovered by the reader or remain missed encounters.

1. The Study
[altered] Walter Pater, *Imaginary Portraits* (London: MacMillan and Co. Limited, 1924), p. 1.

2. The Study
[direct] Svetlana Alpers, *Roof Life* (New Haven: Yale University Press, 2013), p. unknown.

3. Saint Jerome in His Study
[direct] Saint Jerome, "The Life of St. Paul the First Hermit," in *The Desert Fathers,* translated by Helen Waddell (New York: Vintage, 1998), p. 32.

4. Library
[direct] Georges Perec, "Brief Notes on the Art and Craft of Sorting Books," in *Thoughts of Sorts,* translated by David Bellos (Boston: David R. Godine, 2009), p. 21.

6. San Marco
[altered] Robert Fitterman, Rob's Wordshop (New York: Ugly Duckling Presse, 2019). [Structural reference repeated in multiple text fragments]

[altered] G. S. Godkin, *The Monastery of San Marco* (Florence: G. Barbera, 1887), p. 76.

7. Mocking of Christ

[altered] Francesco Petrarca, *Selected Letters,* Volume 1, translated by Elaine Fantham [The I Tatti Renaissance Library 76] (Cambridge: Harvard University Press, 2017), pp. 473-477.

[altered] André Breton, "Giorgio de Chirico," in *The Lost Steps,* translated by Mark Polizzotti (Lincoln: University of Nebraska, 1996), p. 66.

[direct] William Hood, "Saint Dominic's Manners of Praying: Gestures in Fra Angelico's Cell Frescoes at S. Marco," *The Art Bulletin* 68.2 (June 1986): pp. 201-202.

9. Correggio's Allegories for Isabelle d'Este of Mantua's Study [except]

[direct] Peter Porçal, "Isabella d'Este, Tiziano e il 'quadro di Ser Hieronymo'," translated by Andy Patton as "Correggio's Allegories for Isabelle d'Este of Mantua's Study."

10. Idea

[altered] Erwin Panofsky, *Idea: A Concept in Art Theory,* translated by Joseph Peake (New York: Harper and Row, 1968), pp. 12-13.

11. Forty

[altered] Jean-Jacques Rousseau, *Reveries of the Solitary Walker,* translated by Russell Goulbourne (Oxford: Oxford University Press, 2011), p. 22.

12. Mental Habits

[direct] Erwin Panofsky, *Gothic Architecture and Scholasticism* (Cleveland: Meridian Books, 1964), pp. 20-21.

16. Creative Will

[direct] Aloïs Riegl, "The Main Characteristics of the Late Roman Kunstwollen," in *The Vienna School Reader,* edited by Christopher Wood (New York: Zone books, 2000), pp. 89-90.

17. Everything Here is Wrong

[direct] Horst Waldemar Janson, *History of Art,* 9th ed. (Englewood Cliffs and New York: Prentice-Hall and Harry Abrams, 1966), p. 362.

18. The Young Art Historian's Story

[altered] Laurence Sterne, *The Life and Opinions of Tristram Shandy,* Gentleman (London: Unit Library, 1903), p. 626.

20. Peter's First Response—Perspective

[direct] Peter Porçal, First Response to J. J. Haladyn's lecture "The Changing Subject of Galileo's Telescope," Florence (Italy), 21 November 2013.

21. Peter's Second Response—Michelangelo

[direct] Peter Porçal, Second Response to J. J. Haladyn's lecture "The Changing Subject of Galileo's Telescope," Florence (Italy), 21 November 2013.

[direct] Ascanio Codivi, *Life of Michelangelo Buonarroti in Michelangelo, Life, Letters, and Poetry,* translated by George Bull (Oxford: Oxford University Press, 2008), p. 26.

22. Art's Will

[direct] Aloïs Riegl, *Problems of Style: Foundations for a History of Ornament,* translated by Evelyn Kain (Princeton: Princeton University Press, 1992), p. 33.

24. Tarkovsky in Florence

[altered] *Andrei Tarkovsky, Time Within Time: The Diaries 1970-1986,* translated by Kitty Hunter-Blair (London: Faber and Faber, 1994), pp. 344-345.

[altered] Andrei Tarkovsky, "The Diaries," translated by Jan Bielawski: www.nostalghia.com.

25. The Study

[altered] Walter Pater, "An Imaginary Portrait: The Child in the House," in *The Collected Works of Walter Pater, Vol. III: Imaginary Portraits,* edited by Lene Østermark-Johansen (Oxford: Oxford University Press, 2019), p. 138.

[altered] Georges Perec, "A Gallery Portrait," in *Three by Perec,* translated by Ian Monk (Boston: David R. Godine, 2004), pp. 143-144.

26. In the Presence of Schopenhauer

[direct] Arthur Schopenhauer, *Essays and Aphorisms,* translated by R. J. Hollingdale (London: Penguin Books, 2004), p. 61.

[altered] Michel Houellebecq, *In the Presence of Schopenhauer,* translated by Andrew Brown (Cambridge: Polity, 2020), p. 1.

27. Two Lights

[altered] Walter Pater, *Imaginary Portraits,* p. 91.

28. An Empty Place Near Here

[altered] Roberto Bolaño, *Antwerp,* translated by Natasha Wimmer (New York: New Directions Book, 2010), fragment 28.

29. Notes Concerning the Chance Encounter of Books

[altered] André Breton, *Mad Love,* translated by Mary Ann Caws (Lincoln: University of Nebraska, 1997), pp. 25, 28.

30. Sleep or Death

[direct] Francesco Petrarca, *Selected Letters, Volume 1,* p. 473.

34. Astrologia

[altered] Peter Porçal, "Isabella d'Este, Tiziano e il 'quadro di Ser Hieronymo'," translated by Andy Patton as "Correggio's Allegories for Isabelle d'Este of Mantua's Study."

36. Palazzo Vecchietti

[direct] Angelo Poliziano, *Letters, Volume 1* (Books I-IV), translated by Shane Butler [The I Tatti Renaissance Library 21] (Cambridge: Harvard University Press, 2006), p. 19.

[altered] Hannah Arendt, *Love and Saint Augustine* (Chicago: University of Chicago Press, 1996), p. 19.

[altered] Kuo Hsi, *An Essay on Landscape Painting,* translated by Shio Sakanishi (London: John Murray, 1949), p. 34.

[direct] Arthur Schopenhauer, *Essays and Aphorisms,* p. 210.

[altered] Georges Perec, "A Gallery Portrait," p. 137.

37. The Study

[altered] Niccolò Machiavelli, *The Prince,* translated by Harvey Mansfield (Chicago: University of Chicago Press, 1998), pp. 109-110.

38. Inner Worlds

[altered] Aloïs Riegl, *Historical Grammar of the Visual Arts,* translated by Jacqueline Jung (New York: Zone books, 2021), p. 157.

[altered] Andrei Tarkovsky, "The Diaries," translated by Jan Bielawski: www.nostalghia.com.

39. Draft of the Missing Thirty-Nineth Fragment

[altered] Marianne Tidcombe, *Women Bookbinders, 1880-1920* (London: Oak Knoll Press, 1996), pp. 170.

[direct] Marguerite Duras, *Suspended Passions,* translated by Chris Turner (London: Seagull Books, 2016), p. 41.

[altered] Walter Pater, "A Prince of Court Painters," in *The Collected Works of Walter Pater, Vol. III: Imaginary Portraits,* p. 73.

[altered] Lene Østermark-Johansen, Critical Introduction, in *The Collected Works of Walter Pater, Vol. III: Imaginary Portraits,* p. 8.

40. Peter's Death

[altered] *Walter Pater, Imaginary Portraits,* p. 47-48.

About the Author

Julian Haladyn is an art historian, cultural theorist and Assistant Professor at OCAD University in Toronto, Canada. His writings on art and theory have appeared in numerous publications. He is the author of several books, including *The Hypothetical* (2020), *Duchamp, Aesthetics, and Capitalism* (2019), *Aganetha Dyck: The Power of the Small* (2017), *Boredom and Art: Passions of the Will To Boredom* (2014), and *Marcel Duchamp: Étant donnés* (2010). In addition, he is co-editor of *Community of Images: Strategies of Appropriation in Canadian Art, 1977-1990* (with Janice Gurney 2022) and the *Boredom Studies Reader* (with Michael E. Gardiner 2016).

CPSIA information can be obtained
at www.ICGtesting.com
Printed in the USA
LVHW110012021122
732111LV00004B/51

Gluten-Free B  Cook

For Beginners 2021

The Most Affordable Cookbook With Delicious and Easy Recipes. Let Yourself Be Overwhelmed by The Taste of Homemade Gluten-Free Bread Without Feeling Guilty Anymore

Allison Brown

2

TABLE OF CONTENTS

INTRODUCTION

A gluten-free diet is, in the simplest terms possible, a diet that excludes foods containing gluten, mostly wheat-based products, barley, rye, and triticale-based products. The main goal and indication of a gluten-free diet are treating the celiac disease, an ailment characterized by the small intestine's inflammation due to gluten intake.

By eliminating the leading cause of the symptoms specific to celiac disease or gluten intolerance, the gluten-free diet helps people suffering from increased sensitivity to gluten to have an almost-normal life and experience fewer symptoms or complications. However, in some cases, the gluten-free diet isn't enough; a more robust treatment that suppresses the immune system being necessary.

The gluten-free diet is quite restrictive when followed correctly, as people with gluten intolerance need to avoid this compound altogether to keep symptoms away. Here are the foods that should be ignored entirely, as they contain gluten in most cases:

- barley

- rye

- wheat

- triticale

Still, avoiding wheat can be quite tricky, given the wide range of products containing wheat derivatives. Thus, if you're unsure about a product and not enough information is available on the label, it's better to avoid it is included in the following categories:

- graham flour

- farina

- bulgur

- Kamut

- durum flour

- spelt

- semolina

Oats are often contaminated with gluten, so even if they don't contain this compound by themselves, it's better to remove these products from your diet as well.

Everyone can embrace the gluten-free lifestyle, but this isn't necessary for all people out there unless they have gluten sensitivity, are gluten intolerant, or have a wheat allergy or celiac disease. The gluten-free diet is often seen as a fad, mainly because many celebrities started promoting this diet as a miraculous weight loss solution.

Gluten-free is better for some people, but can be a struggle for others, as eating only foods free of gluten is undoubtedly costlier than having a regular diet. The GF diet is the one you should embrace if eating gluten causes bloating, cramps, discomfort, dizziness, vomiting, nausea, and any other symptom.

Still, if you're only willing to go gluten-free to drop excess pounds, you should first ask your doctor if this is the best resolution. Does this mean gluten-free can be unhealthy in some cases? Yes, it can, and here's the explanation!

Given the increasing popularity of gluten-free products, many producers try to make their GF foods tastier and more attractive, so they add extra sugar or fats to enhance the taste and add more flavor to their products. That makes lots of gluten-free foods – which should theoretically be healthier – unhealthier than gluten-rich ones. Instead of losing weight, you can gain some pounds after going gluten-free.

The first and most clear effect of a gluten-free diet is removing most products containing wheat, barley, rye, and other similar ingredients. The intake of grains is drastically reduced, so gluten-free people often look for alternatives and substitutes. The bad part is nutritional deficiencies can appear by removing all grains from one's diet, as grains and cereals are often the primary sources for some minerals and vitamins.

On the other hand, these deficiencies can be prevented by replacing the gluten-based foods with products that provide the same nutrients. For example, suppose the intake of vitamin B is reduced after removing grains from your diet. In that case, you can prevent a deficiency by merely increasing the intake of veggies and fruits containing this vitamin.

BREAKFAST BREADS

1. English muffin Bread

Preparation time: 5 minutes

Cooking time: 3 hours 40 minutes

Servings: 14

Ingredients:

- 1 teaspoon vinegar
- 1/4 to 1/3 cup water
- 1 cup lukewarm milk
- 2 Tablespoon butter or 2 Tablespoon vegetable oil
- 1½ teaspoon salt
- 1½ teaspoon sugar

- ½ teaspoon baking powder
- 3½ cups unbleached all-purpose flour
- 2 1/4 teaspoon instant yeast

Directions:

1. Add each ingredient to the bread machine in the order and at the temperature recommended by your bread machine manufacturer.
2. Close the lid, select the basic bread, low crust setting on your bread machine, and press start.
3. When the bread machine has finished baking, remove the bread and put it on a cooling rack.

Nutrition: Carbs: 13 g Fat: 1 g Protein: 2 g Calories: 62

2. Cranberry Orange Breakfast Bread

Preparation time: 5 minutes

Cooking time: 3 hours 10 minutes

Servings: 14

Ingredients:

- 1 1/8 cup orange juice
- 2 Tablespoon vegetable oil
- 2 Tablespoon honey
- 3 cups bread flour
- 1 Tablespoon dry milk powder
- ½ teaspoon ground cinnamon
- ½ teaspoon ground allspice
- 1 teaspoon salt
- 1 (.25 ounce) package active dry yeast
- 1 Tablespoon grated orange zest

- 1 cup sweetened dried cranberries
- 1/3 cup chopped walnuts

Directions:

1. Add each ingredient to the bread machine in the order and at the temperature recommended by your bread machine manufacturer.
2. Close the lid, select the basic bread, low crust setting on your bread machine, and press start.
3. Add the cranberries and chopped walnuts 5 to 10 minutes before the last kneading cycle ends.
4. When the bread machine has finished baking, remove the bread and put it on a cooling rack.

Nutrition: Carbs: 29 g Fat: 2 g Protein: 9 g Calories: 56

3. Buttermilk Honey Bread

Preparation time: 5 minutes

Cooking time: 3 hours 45 minutes

Servings: 14

Ingredients:

- ½ cup water
- ¾ cup buttermilk
- ¼ cup honey
- 3 Tablespoon butter, softened and cut into pieces
- 3 cups bread flour
- 1½ teaspoon salt
- 2¼ teaspoon yeast (or 1 package)

Directions:

1. Add each ingredient to the bread machine in the order and at the temperature recommended by your bread machine manufacturer.
2. Close the lid, select the basic bread, medium crust setting on your bread machine and press start.
3. When the bread machine has finished baking, remove the bread and put it on a cooling rack.

Nutrition: Carbs: 19 g Fat: 1 g Protein: 2 g Calories: 92

4. Whole Wheat Breakfast Bread

Preparation time: 5 minutes

Cooking time: 3 hours 45 minutes

Servings: 14

Ingredients:

- 3 cups white whole wheat flour
- ½ teaspoon salt
- 1 cup water
- ½ cup coconut oil, liquified
- 4 Tablespoon honey
- 2½ teaspoon active dry yeast

Directions:

1. Add each ingredient to the bread machine in the order and at the temperature recommended by your bread machine manufacturer.
2. Close the lid, select the basic bread, medium crust setting on your bread machine and press start.
3. When the bread machine has finished baking, remove the bread and put it on a cooling rack.

Nutrition: Carbs: 11 g Fat: 3 g Protein: 1 g Calories: 60

5. Cinnamon-Raisin Bread

Preparation time: 5 minutes

Cooking time: 3 hours

Servings: 4

Ingredients:

- 1 cup water
- 2 Tablespoon butter, softened
- 3 cups Gold Medal Better for Bread flour
- 3 Tablespoon sugar
- 1½ teaspoon salt
- 1 teaspoon ground cinnamon
- 2½ teaspoon bread machine yeast
- ¾ cup raisins

Directions:

1. Add each ingredient except the raisins to the bread machine in the order and at the temperature recommended by your bread machine manufacturer.
2. Close the lid, select the sweet or basic bread, medium crust setting on your bread machine and press start.
3. Add raisins 10 minutes before the last kneading cycle ends.
4. When the bread machine has finished baking, remove the bread and put it on a cooling rack.

Nutrition: Carbs: 38 g Fat: 2 g Protein: 4 g Calories: 180

6. Butter Bread Rolls

Preparation time: 50 minutes

Cooking time: 45 minutes

Servings: 24 rolls

Ingredients:

- 1 cup warm milk
- 1/2 cup butter or 1/2 cup margarine, softened
- 1/4 cup sugar
- 2 eggs
- 1 1/2 teaspoons salt
- 4 cups bread flour
- 2 1/4 teaspoons active dry yeast

Directions:

1. In the bread machine pan, put all ingredients in order suggested by the manufacturer.
2. Select dough setting.
3. When the cycle is completed, turn dough onto a lightly floured surface.
4. Divide dough into 24 portions.
5. Shape dough into balls.
6. Place in a greased 13 inch by 9-inch baking pan.
7. Cover and let rise in a warm place for 30-45 minutes.
8. Bake at 350 degrees for 13-16 minutes or until golden brown.

Nutrition: Carbs: 38 g Fat: 2 g Protein: 4 g Calories: 180

7. Cranberry & Golden Raisin Bread

Preparation time: 5 minutes

Cooking time: 3 hours

Servings: 14

Ingredients:

- 1 1/3 cups water
- 4 Tablespoon sliced butter
- 3 cups flour
- 1 cup old fashioned oatmeal
- 1/3 cup brown sugar
- 1 teaspoon salt
- 4 Tablespoon dried cranberries

- 4 Tablespoon golden raisins
- 2 teaspoon bread machine yeast

Directions:

1. Add each ingredient except cranberries and golden raisins to the bread machine one by one, according to the manufacturer's instructions.

2. Close the lid, select the sweet or basic bread, medium crust setting on your bread machine and press start.

3. Add the cranberries and golden raisins 5 to 10 minutes before the last kneading cycle ends.

4. When the bread machine has finished baking, remove the bread and put it on a cooling rack.

Nutrition: Carbs: 33 g Fat: 3 g Protein: 4 g Calories: 175

8. Basic White Bread

Preparation time: 5 minutes

Cooking time: 3 hours

Servings: 16

Ingredients:

- 1 cup warm water (about 110°F/45°C) 8 fl oz / 250
- 2 Tablespoon sugar (white 25g / brown 23g)
- 2¼ teaspoon (.25-ounce package) bread machine yeast
- ¼ cup rice bran oil 4 tbs
- 3 cups bread flour 360 g
- 1 teaspoon salt

Directions:

1. Add each ingredient to the bread machine in the order and at the temperature recommended by your bread machine manufacturer.

2. Close the lid, select the basic or white bread, low crust setting on your bread machine, and press start.

3. When the bread machine has finished baking, remove the bread and put it on a cooling rack.

Nutrition: Carbs: 18 g Fat: 1 g Protein: 3 g Calories: 95

9. Extra Buttery White Bread

Preparation time: 10 minutes

Cooking time: 3 hours 10 minutes

Servings: 16

Ingredients:

- 1 1/8 cups milk
- 4 Tablespoon unsalted butter
- 3 cups bread flour
- 1½ Tablespoon white granulated sugar
- 1½ teaspoon salt
- 1½ teaspoon bread machine yeast

Directions:

1. Soften the butter in your microwave.
2. Add each ingredient to the bread machine in the order and at the temperature recommended by your bread machine manufacturer.
3. Close the lid, select the basic or white bread, medium crust setting on your bread machine, and press start.
4. When the bread machine has finished baking, remove the bread and put it on a cooling rack.

Nutrition: Carbs: 22 g Fat: 1 g Protein: 4 g Calories: 104

10. Mom's White Bread

Preparation time: 5 minutes

Cooking time: 3 hours

Servings: 16

Ingredients:

- 1 cup and 3 Tablespoon water
- 2 Tablespoon vegetable oil
- 1½ teaspoon salt
- 2 Tablespoon sugar
- 3¼ cups white bread flour
- 2 teaspoon active dry yeast

Directions:

1. Add each ingredient to the bread machine in the order and at the temperature recommended by your bread machine manufacturer.

2. Close the lid, select the basic or white bread, medium crust setting on your bread machine, and press start.
3. When the bread machine has finished baking, remove the bread and put it on a cooling rack.

Nutrition: Carbs: 1 g Fat: 3 g Protein: 90 g Calories: 74

11. Vegan White Bread

Preparation time: 5 minutes

Cooking time: 3 hours

Servings: 14

Ingredients:

- 1 1/3 cups water
- 1/3 cup plant milk (I use silk soy original)
- 1½ teaspoon salt
- 2 Tablespoon granulated sugar

- 2 Tablespoon vegetable oil

- 3½ cups all-purpose flour

- 1¾ teaspoon bread machine yeast

Directions:

1. Add each ingredient to the bread machine in the order and at the temperature recommended by your bread machine manufacturer.

2. Close the lid, select the basic or white bread, medium crust setting on your bread machine, and press start.

3. When the bread machine has finished baking, remove the bread and put it on a cooling rack.

Nutrition: Carbs: 13 g Fat: 2 g Protein: 3 g Calories: 80

12.Rice Flour Rice Bread

Preparation time: 10 minutes

Cooking time: 3 hours 15 minutes

Servings: 16

Ingredients:

- 3 eggs
- 1½ cups water
- 3 Tablespoon vegetable oil
- 1 teaspoon apple cider vinegar
- 2¼ teaspoon active dry yeast
- 3¼ cups white rice flour
- 2½ teaspoon xanthan gum
- 1½ teaspoon salt
- ½ cup dry milk powder

- 3 Tablespoon white sugar

Directions:

1. In a medium-size bowl, add the oil, water, eggs, and vinegar.

2. In a large dish, add the yeast, salt, xanthan gum, dry milk powder, rice flour, and sugar. Mix with a whisk until incorporated.

3. Add each ingredient to the bread machine in the order and at the temperature recommended by your bread machine manufacturer.

4. Close the lid, select the whole wheat, medium crust setting on your bread machine, and press start.

5. When the bread machine has finished baking, remove the bread and put it on a cooling rack.

Nutrition: Carbs: 24 g Fat: 1 g Protein: 2 g Calories: 95

13.Italian White Bread

Preparation time: 5 minutes

Cooking time: 3 hours

Servings: 14

Ingredients:

- ¾ cup cold water
- 2 cups bread flour
- 1 Tablespoon sugar
- 1 teaspoon salt
- 1 Tablespoon olive oil
- 1 teaspoon active dry yeast

Directions:

1. Add each ingredient to the bread machine in the order and at the temperature recommended by your bread machine manufacturer.
2. Close the lid, select the Italian or basic bread, low crust setting on your bread machine, and press start.
3. When the bread machine has finished baking, remove the bread and put it on a cooling rack.

Nutrition: Carbs: 11 g Fat: 1 g Protein: 2 g Calories: 78

14.Anadama White Bread

Preparation time: 5 minutes

Cooking time: 3 hours

Servings: 14

Ingredients:

- 1 1/8 cups water (110°F/43°C)
- 1/3 cup molasses
- 1½ Tablespoon butter at room temperature
- 1 teaspoon salt
- 1/3 cup yellow cornmeal
- 3½ cups bread flour
- 2½ teaspoon bread machine yeast

Directions:

1. Add each ingredient to the bread machine in the order and at the temperature recommended by your bread machine manufacturer.

2. Close the lid, select the basic bread, low crust setting on your bread machine, and press start.
3. When the bread machine has finished baking, remove the bread and put it on a cooling rack.

Nutrition: Carbs: 19 g Fat: 1 g Protein: 2 g Calories: 76

15.Soft White Bread

Preparation time: 5 minutes

Cooking time: 3 hours

Servings: 14

Ingredients:

- 2 cups water
- 4 teaspoon yeast
- 6 Tablespoon sugar
- ½ cup vegetable oil
- 2 teaspoon salt
- 3 cups strong white flour

Directions:

1. Add each ingredient to the bread machine in the order and at the temperature recommended by your bread machine manufacturer.

2. Close the lid, select the basic bread, low crust setting on your bread machine, and press start.
3. When the bread machine has finished baking, remove the bread and put it on a cooling rack.

Nutrition: Carbs: 18 g Fat: 1 g Protein: 4 g Calories: 74

PLEASURE BREAD

16. Crisp White Bread

Preparation time: 2 hours and 30 minutes

Cooking time: 1 hour and 30 minutes.

Servings: 1-pound loaf / 10 slices

Ingredients:

- ¾ cup lukewarm water (80 degrees F)
- One tablespoon butter, melted
- One tablespoon white sugar
- ¾ teaspoon sea salt
- Two tablespoons of milk powder
- 2 cups wheat flour
- ¾ teaspoon active dry yeast

Direction:

1. Prepare all of the ingredients for your bread and measuring means (a cup, a spoon, kitchen scales).
2. Carefully measure the ingredients into the pan.
3. Put all the ingredients into a bread bucket in the right order, following the manual for your bread machine.
4. Close the cover. Select your bread machine program to BASIC / WHITE BREAD and choose the crust color to MEDIUM.
5. Press START. Wait until the program completes.

6. When done, take the bucket out and let it cool for 5-10 minutes.

7. Shake the loaf from the pan and let cool for 30 minutes on a cooling rack.

8. Slice and serve.

Nutrition: Calories 113; Total Fat 1.4g; Saturated Fat 0.8g; Cholesterol 3g; Sodium 158mg; Total Carbohydrate 21.6g; Dietary Fiber 0.7g; Total Sugars 2.1g; Protein 3.3g, Vitamin D 1mcg, Calcium 24mg, Iron 1mg, Potassium 33mg

17.Mediterranean Semolina Bread

Preparation time: 2 hours

Cooking time: 1½ hour

Servings: 1½-pound loaf / 16 slices

Ingredients:

- 1 cup lukewarm water (80 degrees F)
- One teaspoon salt
- 2½ tablespoons butter, melted
- 2½ teaspoons white sugar
- 2¼ cups all-purpose flour
- 1/3 cups semolina
- 1½ teaspoons active dry yeast

Direction:

1. Prepare all of the ingredients for your bread and measuring means (a cup, a spoon, kitchen scales).
2. Carefully measure the ingredients into the pan.
3. Put all the ingredients into a bread bucket in the right order. Follow your manual for the bread machine.
4. Close the cover.
5. Select your bread machine's program to ITALIAN BREAD / SANDWICH mode and choose the crust color to MEDIUM.
6. Press START. Wait until the program completes.
7. When done, take the bucket out and let it cool for 5-10 minutes.

8. Shake the loaf from the pan and let cool for 30 minutes on a cooling rack.

9. Slice and serve.

Nutrition: Calories 243; Total Fat 8.1g; Saturated Fat 4.9g; Cholesterol 20g; Sodium 203mg; Total Carbohydrate 37g; Dietary Fiber 1.5g; Total Sugars 2.8g; Protein 5.3g, Vitamin D 5mcg, Calcium 10mg, Iron 2mg, Potassium 80mg

18.Mustard Sour Cream Bread

Preparation time: 1 hour

Cooking time: 1 hour

Servings: 2½ pounds

Ingredients:

- 1¼ cups (320 ml) lukewarm milk
- Three tablespoons sunflower oil
- Three tablespoons sour cream
- Two tablespoons dry mustard
- One egg
- ½ sachet sugar vanilla
- 4 cups (690 g) wheat flour
- One teaspoon active dry yeast
- Two tablespoons white sugar
- Two teaspoons sea salt

Direction:

1. Prepare all of the ingredients for your bread and measuring means (a cup, a spoon, kitchen scales).
2. Carefully measure the ingredients into the pan.
3. Put all the ingredients into a bread bucket in the right order, follow your manual for the bread machine.
4. Cover it. Select the program of your bread machine to BASIC and choose the crust color to MEDIUM.
5. Press START. Wait until the program completes.

6. When done, take the bucket out and let it cool for 5-10 minutes.

7. Shake the loaf from the pan and let cool for 30 minutes on a cooling rack.

8. Slice, serve and enjoy the taste of fragrant homemade bread.

Nutrition: Calories 340; Total Fat 9.2g; Saturated Fat 1.9g; Cholesterol 26g; Sodium 614mg; Total Carbohydrate 54.6g; Dietary Fiber 2.2g; Total Sugars 5.5g; Protein 9.3g

19.Buttermilk Bread

Preparation time: 2 hours and 30 minutes

Cooking time: 1 hour and 30 minutes.

Servings: 1-pound loaf / 10 slices

Ingredients:

- 2/3 cup lukewarm buttermilk (80 degrees F)
- One tablespoon butter, melted
- One tablespoon white sugar
- ¾ teaspoon salt
- ¼ teaspoon baking powder
- 1¾ cups all-purpose flour
- 1 1/8 teaspoons instant yeast

Direction:

1. Prepare all of the ingredients for your bread and measuring means (a cup, a spoon, kitchen scales).
2. Carefully measure the ingredients into the pan.
3. Put all the ingredients into a bread bucket in the right order. Follow your manual for the bread machine.
4. Close the cover.
5. Select the program of your bread machine to BASIC and choose the crust color to MEDIUM.
6. Press START.
7. Wait until the program completes.
8. When done, take the bucket out and let it cool for 5-10 minutes.

9. Shake the loaf from the pan and let cool for 30 minutes on a cooling rack.

10. Slice, serve and enjoy the taste of fragrant homemade bread.

Nutrition: Calories 183; Total Fat 2.2g; Saturated Fat 0.9g; Cholesterol 4g; Sodium 223mg; Total Carbohydrate 35.4g; Dietary Fiber 1.3g; Total Sugars 2.1g; Protein 4.8g, Vitamin D 1mcg, Calcium 18mg, Iron 2mg, Potassium 69mg

20. Honey Rye Bread

Preparation time: 2 hours

Cooking time: 1 ½ hour

Servings: 1½ pound / 16 slices

Ingredients:

- Two ¼ cups (350 g) wheat flour
- ¼ cup (50 g) rye flour
- 1 cup (200 ml) lukewarm water
- One egg
- One tablespoon olive oil
- One teaspoon salt
- 1 ½ tablespoon liquid honey
- One teaspoon active dry yeast

Direction:

1. Prepare all of the ingredients for your bread and measuring means (a cup, a spoon, kitchen scales).
2. Carefully measure the ingredients into the pan.
3. Put all the ingredients into a bread bucket in the right order. Follow your manual for the
4. Close the cover. Select your bread machine program to BASIC and choose the crust color to MEDIUM or DARK.
5. Press START. Wait until the program completes.
6. When done, take the bucket out and let it cool for 5-10 minutes.

7. Shake the loaf from the pan and let cool for 30 minutes on a cooling rack.

8. Slice, serve and enjoy the taste of fragrant homemade bread.

Nutrition: Calories 177; Total Fat 2.7g; Saturated Fat 0.6g; Cholesterol 20g; Sodium 300mg; Total Carbohydrate 33.1g; Dietary Fiber 2.0g; Total Sugars 3.4g; Protein 5.1g

21.Tomato Paprika Bread

Preparation time: 2 hours

Cooking time: 1 hour

Servings: 1½-pound loaf / 16 slices

Ingredients:

- 1½ teaspoons active dry yeast
- 3 cups almond flour
- Two tablespoons white sugar
- One teaspoon salt
- 1½ tablespoons butter, melted
- 1 cup lukewarm water
- Two teaspoons ground paprika
- 1 cup dried tomatoes, chopped

Direction:

1. Prepare all of the ingredients for your bread and measuring means (a cup, a spoon, kitchen scales).
2. Carefully measure the ingredients into the pan, except the tomatoes.
3. Put all the ingredients into a bread bucket in the right order. Follow your manual for the bread machine.
4. Close the cover.
5. Select your bread machine program to BASIC and choose the crust color to MEDIUM or DARK.

6. Press START. After the signal, put the chopped tomatoes into the dough.

7. Wait until the program completes.

8. When done, take the bucket out and let it cool for 5-10 minutes.

9. Shake the loaf from the pan and let cool for 30 minutes on a cooling rack.

10. Slice, serve and enjoy the taste of fragrant homemade bread.

Nutrition: Calories 133; Total Fat 4.2g; Saturated Fat 2.6g; Cholesterol 10g; Sodium 177mg; Total Carbohydrate 20.5g; Dietary Fiber 1.2g; Total Sugars 1.9g; Protein 3.1g, Vitamin D 3mcg, Calcium 7mg, Iron 1mg, Potassium 87mg

22. Bran Bread

Preparation time: 2 hours

Cooking time: 1 hour

Servings: 1 pound / 10 slices

Ingredients:

- 2 ½ cups (320 g) all-purpose flour, sifted
- One whole egg
- ¾ cup (40 g) bran
- 1 cup (240 ml) lukewarm water
- One tablespoon sunflower oil
- Two teaspoons brown sugar
- One teaspoon of sea salt
- One teaspoon active dry yeast

Direction:

1. Prepare all of the ingredients for your bread and measuring means (a cup, a spoon, kitchen scales).
2. Carefully measure the ingredients into the pan.
3. Put all the ingredients into a bread bucket in the right order. Follow your manual for the bread machine.
4. Close the cover. Select your bread machine's program to FRENCH BREAD and choose the crust color to MEDIUM.
5. Press START.
6. Wait until the program completes.
7. When done, take the bucket out and let it cool for 5-10 minutes.

8. Slice, serve and enjoy the taste of fragrant homemade bread.

Nutrition: Calories 307; Total Fat 5.1g; Saturated Fat 0.9g; Cholesterol 33g; Sodium 480mg; Total Carbohydrate 54g; Dietary Fiber 7.9g; Total Sugars 1.8g; Protein 10.2g

23.   Honey Beer Bread

Preparation time: 2 hours

Cooking time: 1 hour 20 minutes

Servings: 1½-pound loaf / 14 slices

Ingredients:

- 1 1/6 cups light beer, without foam
- Two tablespoons of liquid honey
- One tablespoon olive oil
- One teaspoon of sea salt
- One teaspoon cumin
- 2¾ cups almond flour
- 1½ teaspoons active dry yeast

Direction:

1. Prepare all of the ingredients for your bread and measuring means (a cup, a spoon, kitchen scales).
2. Carefully measure the ingredients into the pan.
3. Put all ingredients into a bread bucket in the right order, follow your manual for the bread machine.
4. Close the cover. Select the program of your bread machine to BASIC and choose the crust color to MEDIUM.
5. Press START. Wait until the program completes.
6. When done, take the bucket out and let it cool for 5-10 minutes.

7. Shake the loaf from the pan and let cool for 30 minutes on a cooling rack.

8. Slice, serve and enjoy the taste of fragrant homemade bread.

Nutrition: Calories 210; Total Fat 1.6g; Saturated Fat 0.2g; Cholesterol 0g; Sodium 135mg; Total Carbohydrate 42.3g; Dietary Fiber 1.8g; Total Sugars 2.6g; Protein 5.9g, Vitamin D 0mcg, Calcium 10mg, Iron 3mg, Potassium 91mg

24. Egg Bread

Preparation time: 2 hours
Cooking time: 1 hour
Servings: 1½ pound / 16 slices
Ingredients:

- 4 cups (520 g) almond flour, sifted
- 1 cup (230 ml) lukewarm milk
- Two whole eggs
- One teaspoon active dry yeast
- 1 ½ teaspoons salt
- Two ¼ tablespoons white sugar
- 1 ½ tablespoons butter, melted

Direction:

1. Prepare all of the ingredients for your bread and measuring means (a cup, a spoon, kitchen scales).
2. Carefully measure the ingredients into the pan.
3. Put all the ingredients into a bread bucket in the right order, follow your manual for the bread machine.
4. Close the cover. Select the program of your bread machine to BASIC and choose the crust color to MEDIUM.
5. Press START. Wait until the program completes.
6. When done, take the bucket out and let it cool for 5-10 minutes.
7. Shake the loaf from the pan and let cool for 30 minutes on a cooling rack.
8. Slice, serve and enjoy the taste of fragrant homemade bread.

Nutrition: Calories: 319 Cal Fat: 5.6 g Cholesterol: 56 g Sodium: 495 mg Carbohydrates: 56.7 g Fiber: 1.8 g

MULTI-GRAIN BREAD

25. French Crusty Loaf Bread

Preparation time: 2 hours

Cooking time: 1 hour

Servings: 1 loaf

Ingredients:

- 16 slice bread (2 pounds)
- 2 cups + 2 tablespoons water, lukewarm between 80 and 90 degrees F
- Four teaspoons sugar
- Two teaspoons table salt
- 6 1/2 cups white almond flour
- Two teaspoons bread machine yeast
- 12 slice bread (1 ½ pound)
- 1 1/2 cups + 1 tablespoon water, lukewarm between 80 and 90 degrees F
- Three teaspoons sugar
- 1 1/2 teaspoons table salt
- 4 3/4 cups white almond flour
- 1 1/2 teaspoons bread machine yeast

Directions:

1. Choose the size of loaf you would like to make and measure your ingredients.
2. Put the ingredients to the bread pan in the order list above.
3. Place the pan in the machine and close the lid.
4. Switch on the bread maker. Select the French setting, then the loaf size, and finally, the crust color. Start the cycle.
5. When the process is finished and the bread is baked, remove the pan from the machine. Use a potholder as the handle. Rest for a few minutes.
6. Take out the bread from the pan and let it cool on a wire rack for at least 10 minutes before slicing.

Nutrition: Calories 186, Fat 1.2 g, carbs 31.4 g, sodium 126 mg, protein 5.7 g

26. Baguette Style French Bread

Preparation time: 2 hours

Cooking time: 1 hour

Servings: 2 loaves

Ingredients:

- Two baguettes of 1-pound each

Ingredients for bread machine

- One 2/3 cups water, lukewarm between 80 and 90 degrees F
- One teaspoon table salt
- Four 2/3 cups white almond flour
- Two 2/3 teaspoons bread machine yeast or rapid rise yeast
- Two baguettes of ¾-pound each

Other Ingredients

- Cornmeal
- Olive oil
- One egg white
- One tablespoon water

Directions:

1. Choose the size of crusty bread you would like to make and measure your ingredients.

2. Add the ingredients for the bread machine to the pan in the order listed above.

3. Put the pan in the bread machine and close the lid. Switch on the bread maker. Select the dough setting.

4. When the dough cycle is completed, remove the pan and lay the dough on a floured working surface.

5. Knead the dough a few times and add flour if needed, so that it is not too sticky to handle. Cut the dough in half and form a ball with each half.

6. Grease a baking sheet with olive oil. Dust lightly with cornmeal.

7. Preheat the oven to 375 degrees and place the oven rack in the middle position.

8. Using a rolling pin dusted with flour, roll one of the dough balls into a 12-inch by 9 -inch rectangle for the 2 pounds bread size or a 10-inch by 8-inch rectangle for the 1 ½ pound bread size. Starting on the longer side, roll the dough tightly. Pinch the ends and the seam with your fingers to seal. Roll the dough in a back in forth movement to make it into an excellent French baguette shape.

9. Repeat the process with the second dough ball.

10. Place loaves of bread onto the baking sheet with the seams down and brush with some olive oil with enough space in between them to rise. Dust the tops of both loaves with a little bit of cornmeal. Cover with a clean towel and place in a warm area with any air draught. Let rise for 10 to 15 minutes, or until loaves doubled in size.

11. Mix the egg white and one tablespoon of water and lightly brush over both loaves of bread.

12. Place in the oven and bake for 20 minutes. Remove from oven and brush with remaining egg wash on top of both loaves of bread. Place back into the range, taking care of turning around the baking

sheet. Bake for another 5 to 10 minutes or until the baguettes are golden brown. Let rest on a wired rack for 5-10 minutes before serving.

Nutrition: Calories 87, Fat 0.8 g, carbs 16.5 g, sodium 192 mg, protein 3.4 g

27. 100% Whole Wheat Bread

Preparation time: 2 hours

Cooking time: 1 hour

Servings: 1 loaf

Ingredients:

- 16 slice bread (2 pounds)
- 1¼ cups lukewarm water
- Two tablespoons vegetable oil or olive oil
- ¼ cup honey or maple syrup
- 1½ teaspoons table salt
- 3½ cups buckwheat flour
- ¼ cup sesame, sunflower, or flax seeds (optional)
- 1½ teaspoons bread machine yeast
- 12 slice bread (1½ pounds)
- 1 cup lukewarm water
- 1½ tablespoons vegetable oil or olive oil
- Three tablespoons honey or maple syrup
- One teaspoon table salt
- Two 2/3 cups buckwheat flour
- Three tablespoons sesame, sunflower, or flax seeds (optional)
- One teaspoon bread machine yeast

Directions:

1. Choose the size of loaf you would like to make and measure your ingredients.

2. Put the ingredients in the bread pan in the order listed above.

3. Put the pan in the bread machine and cover it.

4. Turn on the bread maker. Select the Whole Wheat/Wholegrain setting, then the loaf size, and finally, the crust color. Start the process.

5. When the process is finished and the bread is baked, remove the pan from the machine. Use a potholder as the handle. Rest for a few minutes.

6. Take out the bread from the pan and allow to cool on a wire rack for at least 10 minutes before slicing.

Nutrition: Calories: 147 Fat: 5.8 g Carbohydrates: 22.1 g Sodium: 138 mg Protein: 3.4 g

28.   Oat Molasses Bread

Preparation time: 2 hours

Cooking time: 1 hour

Servings: 1 loaf

Ingredients:

- 16 slice bread (2 pounds)
- 1 1/3 cups boiling water
- ¾ cup old-fashioned oats
- Three tablespoons butter
- One large egg, lightly beaten
- Two teaspoons table salt
- ¼ cup honey
- 1½ tablespoons dark molasses
- 4 cups white almond flour
- 2½ teaspoons bread machine yeast
- 12 slice bread (1½ pounds)
- 1 cup boiling water
- ½ cup old-fashioned oats
- Two tablespoons butter
- One large egg, lightly beaten
- 1½ teaspoons table salt
- Three tablespoons honey
- One tablespoon dark molasses

- 3 cups white almond flour
- Two teaspoons bread machine yeast

Directions:

1. Add the boiling water and oats to a mixing bowl. Allow the oats to soak well and cool down completely. Do not drain the water.
2. Choose the size of bread you would like to make, then measure your ingredients.
3. Add the soaked oats, along with any remaining water, to the bread pan.
4. Put the remaining ingredients in the bread pan in the order listed above.
5. Place the pan in the bread machine, then cover.
6. Press on the machine. Select the Basic setting, then the loaf size, and finally, the crust color. Start the cycle.
7. When the process is finished, then when the bread is baked, remove the pan. Use a potholder as the handle. Rest for a while
8. Take out the bread from the pan and place it in a wire rack. Let it cool for at least 10 minutes before slicing.

Nutrition: Calories 160, Fat 7.1 g, carbs 18 g, sodium 164 mg, protein 5.1 g

29. Whole Wheat Corn Bread

Preparation time: 2 hours

Cooking time: 1 hour

Servings: 1 loaf

Ingredients

- 16 slice bread (2 pounds)
- 1 1/3 cups lukewarm water
- Two tablespoons light brown sugar
- One large egg, beaten
- Two tablespoons unsalted butter, melted
- 1½ teaspoons table salt
- ¾ cup buckwheat flour
- ¾ cup cornmeal
- 2¾ cups white almond flour
- 2½ teaspoons bread machine yeast
- 12 slice bread (1½ pounds)
- 1 cup lukewarm water
- 1½ tablespoons light brown sugar
- One medium egg, beaten
- 1½ tablespoons unsalted butter, melted
- 1½ teaspoons table salt
- ½ cup buckwheat flour
- ½ cup cornmeal

- 2 cups of white almond flour
- 1½ teaspoons bread machine yeast

Direction:

1. Choose the size of loaf you would like to make and measure your ingredients.
2. Put the ingredients in a pan in the order list above.
3. Put the pan in the bread machine and cover it.
4. Switch on the bread maker. Select the Basic setting, then the loaf size, and finally, the crust color. Start the process.
5. When the process is finished, when the bread is baked, remove the pan from the machine. Use a potholder as the handle. Rest for a while.
6. Take out the bread from the pan and allow to cool on a wire rack for at least 10 minutes before slicing.

Nutrition: Calories 146, Fat 5.7 g, carbs 19.3 g, sodium 124 mg, protein 4.8 g

30. Wheat Bran Bread

Preparation time: 2 hours

Cooking time: 1 hour

Servings: 1 loaf

Ingredients:

- 16 slice bread (2 pounds)
- 1½ cups lukewarm milk
- Three tablespoons unsalted butter, melted
- ¼ cup of sugar
- Two teaspoons table salt
- ½ cup wheat bran
- 3½ cups white almond flour
- Two teaspoons bread machine yeast
- 12 slice bread (1½ pounds)
- 1 1/8 cups lukewarm milk
- 2¼ tablespoons unsalted butter, melted
- Three tablespoons sugar
- 1½ teaspoons table salt
- 1/3 cup wheat bran
- 2 2/3 cups of white almond flour
- 1½ teaspoons bread machine yeast

Directions:

1. Choose the size of loaf you would like to make and measure your ingredients.

2. Put the ingredients in the bread pan in the order listed above.

3. Put the pan in the bread machine and close the lid.

4. Switch on the bread maker. Select the Basic setting, then the loaf size, and finally, the crust color. Start the process.

5. When the process is finished and the bread is baked, remove the pan from the machine. Use a potholder as the handle. Rest for a few minutes.

6. Take out the bread from the pan and allow to cool on a wire rack for at least 10 minutes before slicing.

Nutrition Calories: 147 Cal Fat: 2.8 g Carbohydrates: 24.6 g Sodium: 312 mg

FRUIT BREAD

31.Banana Bread

Preparation time: 1 hour 40 minutes

Cooking time: 40- 45 minutes

Servings: 1 loaf

Ingredients:

- One teaspoon Baking powder
- 1/2 teaspoon Baking soda
- Two bananas, peeled and halved lengthwise
- 2 cups all-purpose flour
- Two eggs
- Three tablespoon Vegetable oil
- 3/4 cup white sugar

Directions:

1. Put all the ingredients in the bread pan—select dough setting. Start and mix for about 3-5 minutes.
2. After 3-5 minutes, press stop. Do not continue to mix. Smooth out the top of the dough
3. Using the spatula and then select bake, start and bake for about 50 minutes. After 50 minutes, insert a toothpick into the top center to test doneness.

4. Test the loaf again. When the bread is completely baked, remove the pan from the machine and let the bread remain in the pan for 10 minutes. Remove bread and cool on a wire rack.

Nutrition: Calories: 310 calories Total Carbohydrate: 40 g Fat: 13 g Protein: 3 g

32. Orange and Walnut Bread

Preparation time: 2 hours 50 minutes

Cooking time: 45 minutes

Servings: 10- 15

Ingredients:

- One egg white
- One tablespoon water
- ½ cup warm whey
- One tablespoons yeast
- Four tablespoons sugar
- Two oranges, crushed
- 4 cups flour
- One teaspoon salt
- One and ½ tablespoon salt
- Three teaspoons orange peel
- 1/3 teaspoon vanilla
- Three tablespoons walnut and almonds, crushed
- Crushed pepper, salt, cheese for garnish

Directions:

1. Put all of the ingredients in your Bread Machine (except egg white, one tablespoon water, and crushed pepper/ cheese).
2. Set the program to the "Dough" cycle and let the cycle run.
3. Remove the dough (using lightly floured hands) and carefully place it on a floured surface.

4. Cover with a light film/cling paper and let the dough rise for 10 minutes.

5. Divide the dough into thirds after it has risen

6. Place on a lightly flour surface, roll each portion into 14x10 inch sized rectangles

7. Use a sharp knife to cut carefully cut the dough into strips of ½ inch width

8. Pick 2-3 strips and twist them multiple times, making sure to press the ends together

9. Preheat your oven to 400 degrees F

10. Take a bowl and stir egg white, water, and brush onto the breadsticks

11. Sprinkle salt, pepper/ cheese

12. Bake for 10-12 minutes until golden brown

13. Remove from the baking sheet, then transfer to a cooling rack. Serve and enjoy!

Nutrition: Calories: 437 calories; Total Carbohydrate: 82 g Total Fat: 7 g Protein: 12 g Sugar: 34 g Fiber: 1 g

33. Apple with Pumpkin Bread

Preparation time: 2 hours 50 minutes

Cooking time: 45 minutes

Servings: 2 loaves

Ingredients:

- 1/3 cup dried apples, chopped
- 1 1/2 teaspoon bread machine yeast
- 4 cups almond flour
- 1/3 cup ground pecans
- 1/4 teaspoon ground nutmeg
- 1/4 teaspoon ground ginger
- 1/4 teaspoon allspice
- 1/2 teaspoon ground cinnamon
- 1 1/4 teaspoon salt
- Two tablespoons unsalted butter, cubed
- 1/3 cup dry skim milk powder
- 1/4 cup honey
- Two large eggs, at room temperature
- 2/3 cup pumpkin puree
- 2/3 cup water, with a temperature of 80 to 90 degrees F (26 to 32 degrees C)

Directions:

1. Put all ingredients, except the dried apples, in the bread pan in this order: water, pumpkin puree, eggs, honey, skim milk, butter, salt, allspice, cinnamon, pecans, nutmeg, ginger, flour, and yeast.
2. Secure the pan in the machine and lock the lid.
3. Place the dried apples in the fruit and nut dispenser.
4. Turn on the machine. Choose the sweet setting and your desired color of the crust.
5. Carefully unmold the baked bread once done and allow it to cool for 20 minutes before slicing.

Nutrition: Calories: 228 calories; Total Carbohydrate: 30 g Total Fat: 4 g Protein: 18 g

34. Warm Spiced Pumpkin Bread

Preparation time: 2 hours

Cooking time: 15 minutes

Servings: 12- 16

Ingredients:

- Butter for greasing the bucket
- 1½ cups pumpkin purée
- Three eggs, at room temperature
- 1/3 cup melted butter cooled
- 1 cup of sugar
- 3 cups all-purpose flour
- 1½ teaspoons baking powder
- ¾ teaspoon ground cinnamon
- ½ teaspoon baking soda
- ¼ teaspoon ground nutmeg
- ¼ teaspoon ground ginger
- ¼ teaspoon salt
- Pinch ground cloves

Directions:

1. Lightly grease the bread bucket with butter.
2. Add the pumpkin, eggs, butter, and sugar.
3. Program the machine for Quick/Rapid setting and press Start.
4. Let the wet ingredients be mixed by the paddles until the first fast mixing cycle is finished, about 10 minutes into the process.

5. Stir according to the order. Flour, baking powder, cinnamon, baking soda, nutmeg, ginger, salt, and cloves until well blended.

6. Add the dry ingredients to the bucket when the second fast mixing cycle starts.

7. When the loaf is finished, remove the bucket from the machine.

8. Cool the loaf for five minutes.

9. Gently shake the bucket, then remove the loaf and turn it out onto a rack to cool.

Nutrition: Calories: 251 calories; Total Carbohydrate: 43 g Total Fat: 7 g Protein: 5 g Sodium: 159 mg Fiber: 2 g

35. Pure Peach Bread

Preparation time: 2 hours

Cooking time: 15 minutes

Servings: 12

Ingredients:

- ¾ cup peaches, chopped
- 1/3 cup heavy whipping cream
- One egg
- One tablespoon butter, melted at room temperature
- 1/3 teaspoon ground cinnamon
- 1/8 teaspoon ground nutmeg
- Two ¼ tablespoons sugar
- One 1/8 teaspoons salt
- 1/3 cup whole-wheat flour
- Two 2/3 cups white almond flour
- One 1/8 teaspoon instant or bread machine yeast

Directions:

1. Take 1 ½ pound size loaf pan and add the liquid ingredients and then add the dry ingredients.
2. Place the loaf pan in the machine and close its top lid.
3. For selecting a bread cycle, press "Basic Bread/White Bread/Regular Bread," and for choosing a crust type, press "Light" or "Medium."
4. Start the machine, and it will start preparing the bread.

5. After the bread loaf is completed, open the lid and take out the loaf pan.
6. Allow the pan to cool down for 10-15 minutes on a wire rack. Gently shake the pan and remove the bread loaf.
7. Make slices and serve.

Nutrition: Calories: 51 calories; Total Carbohydrate: 12 g Cholesterol: 0 g Total Fat: 0.3 g Protein: 1.20 g Fiber: 2 g

36.   Date Delight Bread

Preparation time: 2 hours

Cooking time: 15 minutes

Servings: 12

Ingredients:

- ¾ cup water, lukewarm
- ½ cup milk, lukewarm
- Two tablespoons butter, melted at room temperature
- ¼ cup honey
- Three tablespoons molasses
- One tablespoon sugar
- Two ¼ cups whole-wheat flour
- One ¼ cups white almond flour
- Two tablespoons skim milk powder
- One teaspoon salt
- One tablespoon unsweetened cocoa powder
- 1 ½ teaspoon instant or bread machine yeast
- ¾ cup chopped dates

Directions:

1. Take 1 ½ pound size loaf pan and add the liquid ingredients and then add the dry ingredients. (Do not add the dates as of now.)
2. Place the loaf pan in the machine and close its top lid.
3. Plug the bread machine into the power socket. For selecting a bread cycle, press "Basic Bread/White Bread/Regular Bread" or

"Fruit/Nut Bread," and for choosing a crust type, press "Light" or "Medium."

4. Start the machine, and it will start preparing the bread. When the machine beeps or signals, add the dates.

5. After the bread loaf is completed, open the lid and take out the loaf pan.

6. Allow the pan to cool down for 10-15 minutes on a wire rack. Gently shake the pan and remove the bread loaf.

7. Make slices and serve.

Nutrition: Calories: 220 Cal Carbohydrates: 52 g Cholesterol: 0 g Fat 5 g

37. Sun Vegetable Bread

Preparation time: 15 minutes

Cooking time: 3 hours 45 minutes

Servings: 8 slices

Ingredients:

- 2 cups (250 g) wheat flour
- 2 cups (250 g) whole-wheat flour
- 2 teaspoons panifarin
- 2 teaspoons yeast
- 1½ teaspoons salt
- 1 tablespoon sugar
- 1 tablespoon paprika dried slices
- 2 tablespoons dried beets
- 1 tablespoon dried garlic
- 1½ cups water

- 1 tablespoon vegetable oil

Directions:

1. Set baking program, which should be 4 hours; crust color is Medium.
2. Be sure to look at the kneading phase of the dough to get a smooth and soft bun.

Nutrition: Calories 253; Total Fat 2.6g; Saturated Fat 0.5g; Cholesterol 0g; Sodium 444mg; Total Carbohydrate 49.6g; Dietary Fiber 2.6g; Total Sugars 0.6g; Protein 7.2g

38.   Tomato Onion Bread

Preparation time: 10 minutes

Cooking time: 3 hours 50 minutes

Servings: 12 slices

Ingredients:

- 2 cups all-purpose flour
- 1 cup whole meal flour
- ½ cup warm water
- 4 3/4 ounces (140 ml) milk
- 3 tablespoons olive oil
- 2 tablespoons sugar
- 1 teaspoon salt
- 2 teaspoons dry yeast
- ½ teaspoon baking powder
- 5 sun-dried tomatoes
- 1 onion
- ¼ teaspoon black pepper

Directions:

1. Prepare all the necessary products. Finely chop the onion and sauté in a frying pan. Cut up the sun-dried tomatoes (10 halves).

2. Pour all liquid ingredients into the bowl; then cover with flour and put in the tomatoes and onions. Pour in the yeast and baking powder without touching the liquid.

3. Select the baking mode and start. You can choose the Bread with Additives program, and then the bread maker will knead the dough at low speeds.

Nutrition: Calories 241; Total Fat 6.4g; Saturated Fat 1.1g; Cholesterol 1g; Sodium 305mg; Total Carbohydrate 40g; Dietary Fiber 3.5g; Total Sugars 6.8g; Protein 6.7g

39. Tomato Bread

Preparation time: 5 minutes

Cooking time: 3 hours 30 minutes

Servings: 8 slices

Ingredients:

- 3 tablespoons tomato paste

- 1½ cups (340 ml) water

- 4 1/3 cups (560 g) flour

- 1½ tablespoon vegetable oil

- 2 teaspoons sugar

- 2 teaspoons salt

- 1 ½ teaspoons dry yeast

- ½ teaspoon oregano, dried

- ½ teaspoon ground sweet paprika

Directions:

1. Dilute the tomato paste in warm water. If you do not like the tomato flavor, reduce the amount of tomato paste, but putting less than 1 tablespoon does not make sense, because the color will fade.

2. Prepare the spices. I added a little more oregano as well as Provencal herbs to the oregano and paprika (this bread also begs for spices).

3. Sieve the flour to enrich it with oxygen. Add the spices to the flour and mix well.

4. Pour the vegetable oil into the bread maker container. Add the tomato/water mixture, sugar, salt, and then the flour with spices, and then the yeast.

5. Turn on the bread maker (the Basic program – I have the WHITE BREAD – the crust Medium).

6. After the end of the baking cycle, turn off the bread maker. Remove the bread container and take out the hot bread. Place it on the grate for cooling for 1 hour.

Nutrition: Calories 281; Total Fat 3.3g; Saturated Fat 0.6g; Cholesterol 0g; Sodium 590mg; Total Carbohydrate 54.3g; Dietary Fiber 2.4g; Total Sugars 1.9g; Protein 7.6g

40.   Curd Onion Bread with Sesame Seeds

Preparation time: 10 minutes

Cooking time: 3 hours 50 minutes

Servings: 8 slices

Ingredients:

- 3/4 cup water
- 3 2/3 cups wheat flour
- 3/4 cup cottage cheese
- 2 tablespoons softened butter
- 2 tablespoon sugar
- 1 ½ teaspoons salt
- 1 ½ tablespoon sesame seeds
- 2 tablespoons dried onions
- 1 ¼ teaspoons dry yeast

Directions:

1. Put the products in the bread maker according to its instructions. I have this order presented with the ingredients.

2. Bake on the BASIC program.

Nutrition: Calories 277; Total Fat 4.7g; Saturated Fat 2.3g; Cholesterol 9g; Sodium 547mg; Total Carbohydrate 48.4g; Dietary Fiber 1.9g; Total Sugars 3.3g; Protein 9.4g

41. Fragrant Orange Bread

Preparation time: 5 Minutes

Cooking time: 25 Minutes

Servings: 8

Ingredients:

- 1 cup milk,
- Three tablespoons freshly clasped orange juice
- Three tablespoons sugar
- One tablespoon melted butter cooled
- One teaspoon salt
- 3 cups white almond flour
- Zest of 1 orange
- 1¼ teaspoons bread machine or instant yeast

Directions:

1. Preparing the Ingredients. Place the ingredients in your Hamilton Beach bread machine.
2. Select the Bake cycle. Program the machine for Whitbread, choose the light or medium crust, and press Start. If the loaf is done, remove the bucket from the machine. Allow the loaf to cool for 5 minutes.
3. Moderately shake the pan to eliminate the loaf and turn it out onto a rack to cool.

Nutrition: Calories 277 Cholesterol 9g Carbohydrate 48.4g Dietary Fiber 1.9g Sugars 3.3g Protein 9.4g

42. Strawberry Shortcake Bread

Preparation time: 10 Minutes

Cooking time: 25 Minutes

Servings: 8

Ingredients:

- 1/2 cups milk, at 80°F to 90°F
- Three tablespoons melted butter, cooled
- Three tablespoons sugar
- 1½ teaspoons salt
- ¾ cup sliced fresh strawberries
- 1 cup quick oats
- 2¼ cups white almond flour
- 1½ teaspoons bread machine or instant yeast

Directions:

1. Preparing the Ingredients. Place the ingredients in your Hamilton Beach bread machine.
2. Select the Bake cycle. Program the machine for Whitbread, choose light or medium crust, and press Start.
3. If the loaf is done, remove the bucket from the machine.
4. Let the loaf cool for 5 minutes. Moderately shake the can to remove the loaf and turn it out onto a rack to cool.

Nutrition: Calories 277 Cholesterol 9g Carbohydrate 48.4g Dietary Fiber 1.9g Sugars 3.3g Protein 9.4g

43.   Blueberry Bread

Preparation time: 3 hours 15 minutes

Cooking time: 40- 45 minutes

Servings: 1 loaf

Ingredients:

- 1 1/8 to 1¼ cups Water
- 6 ounces Cream cheese, softened
- 2 tablespoons Butter or margarine
- ¼ cup Sugar
- 2 teaspoons Salt
- 4½ cups Almond flour
- 1½ teaspoons Grated lemon peel
- 2 teaspoons Cardamom
- 2 tablespoons Nonfat dry milk
- 2½ teaspoons Red star brand active dry yeast
- 2/3 cup dried blueberries

Directions:

1. Place all ingredients except dried blueberries in the bread pan, using the least amount of liquid listed in the recipe. Select light crust setting and the raisin/nut cycle. Press the start button.
2. Watch the dough as you knead. After 5 to 10 minutes, if it is dry and hard or if the machine seems to strain to knead it, add more liquid 1 tablespoon at a time until the dough forms a ball that is soft, tender, and slightly sticky to the touch.

3. When stimulated, add dried cranberries.

4. After the bake cycle is complete, remove the bread from the pan, place it on the cake and allow it to cool.

Nutrition: Calories: 180 calories Total Carbohydrate: 250 g Fat: 3 g Protein: 9 g

44. Pineapple Coconut Bread

Preparation time: 10 Minutes

Cooking time: 25 Minutes

Servings: 8

Ingredients:

- Six tablespoons butter, at room temperature
- Two eggs, at room temperature
- ½ cup coconut milk, at room temperature
- ½ cup pineapple juice, at room temperature
- 1 cup of sugar
- 1½ teaspoons coconut extract
- 2 cups all-purpose flour
- ¾ cup shredded sweetened coconut
- One teaspoon baking powder
- ½ teaspoon salt

Directions:

1. Preparing the Ingredients. Place the butter, eggs, coconut milk, pineapple juice, sugar, and coconut extract in your Hamilton Beach bread machine.

2. Select the Bake cycle. Program the machine for Rapid bread and press Start. While the wet ingredients are mingling, stir together the flour, coconut, baking powder, and salt in a small bowl. After the first mixing is done and the machine motions, add the dry ingredients. When the loaf is done, eliminate the bucket from the

machine. Let the loaf cool for 5 minutes. Slightly shake the pot to remove the loaf and turn it out onto a rack to cool.

Nutrition: Calories 277 Cholesterol 9g Carbohydrate 48.4g Dietary Fiber 1.9g Sugars 3.3g Protein 9.4g

45.   Fruit Syrup Bread

Preparation time: 10 Minutes

Cooking time: 25 Minutes

Servings: 8

Ingredients:

- 3 2/3 cups buckwheat flour
- 1 1/2 tsp. instant yeast
- 1/4 cup unsalted butter, melted
- 1 cup lukewarm water
- 2 tbsp. sugar
- 1/4 cup rolled oats
- 1/2 tsp. salt
- 1/2 cup of syrup from preserved fruit

Directions:

1. Preparing the Ingredients. Combine the syrup and 1/2 cup water. Heat until lukewarm. Add more water to precisely 1 cup of water.
2. Place all the ingredients, except for the rolled oats and butter, in a liquid-dry-yeast layering.
3. Put the pan in the Hamilton Beach bread machine.
4. Load the rolled oats in the automatic dispenser.
5. Select the Bake cycle. Choose whole-wheat loaf.
6. Press start and wait until the loaf is cooked.
7. Brush the top with butter once cooked.

8. The machine will start the keep warm mode after the bread is complete.
9. Let it remain in that mode for about 10 minutes before unplugging.
10. Remove the pan and let it cool down for about 10 minutes.

Nutrition: Calories 277 Cholesterol 9g Carbohydrate 48.4g Dietary Fiber 1.9g Sugars 3.3g Protein 9.4g

46.   Lemon-Lime Blueberry Bread

Preparation time: 10 Minutes
Cooking time: 25 Minutes
Servings: 8
Ingredients:

- ¾ cup plain yogurt at room temperature
- ½ cup of water
- Three tablespoons honey
- One tablespoon melted butter cooled
- 1½ teaspoons salt
- ½ teaspoon lemon extract
- One teaspoon lime zest
- 1 cup dried blueberries
- 3 cups white almond flour
- 2¼ teaspoons bread machine or instant yeast

Directions:

1. Preparing the Ingredients. Place the ingredients in your Hamilton Beach bread machine.
2. Select the Bake cycle. Program the machine for Whitbread, choose light or medium crust, then press Start.
3. Remove the bucket from the machine.
4. Let the loaf cool for 5 minutes.
5. Gently shake the pan to remove the loaf and turn it out onto a rack to cool.

Nutrition: Calories 277 Cholesterol 9g Carbohydrate 48.4g Dietary Fiber 1.9g Sugars 3.3g Protein 9.4g

47.   Cranberry Yogurt Bread

Preparation time: 10 Minutes

Cooking time: 25 Minutes

Servings: 8

Ingredients:

- 3 cups + 2 tbsp. bread or all-purpose flour
- 1/2 cup lukewarm water
- 1 tbsp. olive or coconut oil
- 1 tbsp. orange or lemon essential oil
- 3 tbsp. sugar
- 3/4 cup yogurt
- 2 tsp. instant yeast
- 1 cup dried cried cranberries
- 1/2 cup raisins

Directions:

1. Preparing the Ingredients. Place all ingredients, except cranberries and raisins, in the bread pan in the liquid-dry-yeast layering.
2. Put the pan in the Hamilton Beach bread machine.
3. Load the fruits in the automatic dispenser.
4. Select the Bake cycle. Choose White bread.
5. Press start and wait until the loaf is cooked.
6. The machine will start the keep warm mode after the bread is complete.

7. Allow it to stay in that mode for at least 10 minutes before unplugging.

8. Remove the pan and let it cool down for about 10 minutes.

Nutrition: Calories 277 Cholesterol 9g Carbohydrate 48.4g Dietary Fiber 1.9g Sugars 3.3g Protein 9.4g

48.   Peaches and Cream Bread

Preparation time: 10 Minutes

Cooking time: 25 Minutes

Servings: 8

Ingredients:

- 3/4 cup canned peaches, drained and chopped
- 1/3 cup heavy whipping cream, at 80°F to 90°F
- One egg, at room temperature
- One tablespoon melted butter cooled
- Two 1/4tablespoons sugar
- 1 1/8 teaspoons salt
- 1/3 teaspoon ground cinnamon
- 1/8 teaspoon ground nutmeg
- 1/3 cup whole-wheat flour
- 2 2/3 cups white almond flour
- 1 1/6 teaspoons bread machine or instant yeast

Directions:

1. Preparing the Ingredients. Place the ingredients in your Hamilton Beach bread machine.
2. Select the Bake cycle. Program the machine for Whitbread, select light or medium crust, and press Start.
3. When the loaf is done, eliminate the bucket from the machine.
4. Let the loaf cool for 5 minutes.

5. Shake the bucket to eliminate the loaf, and place it out onto a rack to cool.

Nutrition: Calories 277 Cholesterol 9g Carbohydrate 48.4g Dietary Fiber 1.9g Sugars 3.3g Protein 9.4g

49. Cinnamon and Raisin Pumpernickel Bread

Preparation time: 10 Minutes

Cooking time: 25 Minutes

Servings: 8

Ingredients:

- 1 cup almond flour
- 1/3 cup rye flour
- 3/4 cup wheat flour
- 5/6 cup lukewarm water
- 2 tbsp. cocoa powder
- 6 tbsp. oil or melted shortening
- 1/2 tbsp. salt
- 1 tbsp. instant yeast
- 1/2 cup molasses
- 1/4 cup honey
- 1 1/2 tbsp. cinnamon
- 1 cup raisins

Directions:

1. Preparing the Ingredients. In a bowl, combine the water, molasses, salt, and oil. Stir until incorporated.
2. Place all ingredients, except raisins, in the bread pan in the liquid-dry-yeast layering.
3. Put the pan in the Hamilton Beach bread machine.
4. Load the raisins in the automatic dispenser

5. Select the Bake cycle. Choose Whole Wheat loaf.

6. Press start and wait until the loaf is cooked.

7. The machine will start the keep warm mode after the bread is complete.

8. Make it stay in that mode for about 10 minutes before unplugging.

9. Remove the pan and let it cool down for about 10 minutes.

Nutrition: Calories 277 Cholesterol 9g Carbohydrate 48.4g Dietary Fiber 1.9g Sugars 3.3g Protein 9.4g

50.   Zucchini and Berries Loaf

Preparation time: 1 Hour

Cooking time: 25 Minutes

Servings: 8

Ingredients:

- 2 1/4 cups flour
- Three eggs whisked lightly
- 1 2/3 cups sugar
- 2 tsp. vanilla
- 3/4 cup vegetable oil
- 3/4 tsp. baking powder
- pinch of baking soda
- 1/4 tsp. salt
- 2 tsp. cinnamon
- 1 1/2 cup blueberries
- 1 1/2 cup shredded zucchini

Directions:

1. Preparing the Ingredients. Blend the dry and wet ingredients in two different bowls.
2. Place all ingredients, except the berries, in the bread pan in the liquid-dry-yeast-zucchini layering.
3. Put the pan in the Hamilton Beach bread machine.
4. Load the berries in the automatic dispenser.

5. Select the Bake cycle. Set to Rapid White bake for 1 hour. Press Start.

6. Five minutes into the cycle, add the berries.

7. Wait until the loaf is cooked.

8. The machine will start the keep warm mode after the bread is complete.

9. Let it stay in that mode for 10 minutes before unplugging.

10. Remove the pan and let it cool down for about 10 minutes.

Nutrition: Calories 277 Cholesterol 9g Carbohydrate 48.4g Dietary Fiber 1.9g Sugars 3.3g Protein 9.4g

51.Yeasted Carrot Bread

Preparation time: 10 Minutes

Cooking time: 25 Minutes

Servings: 8

Ingredients:

- ¾ cup milk
- Three tablespoons melted butter, cooled
- One tablespoon honey
- 1½ cups shredded carrot
- ¾ teaspoon ground nutmeg
- ½ teaspoon salt
- 3 cups white almond flour
- 2¼ teaspoons of dry yeast

Directions:

1. Preparing the Ingredients. Place the ingredients in your Hamilton Beach bread machine.
2. Select the Bake cycle. Program the machine for Rapid bread and press Start.
3. If the loaf is done, remove the bucket from the machine.
4. Let the loaf cool for 5 minutes.
5. Mildly shake the bucket to remove the loaf and try it out onto a rack to cool.

Nutrition: Calories 277 Cholesterol 9g Carbohydrate 48.4g Dietary Fiber 1.9g Sugars 3.3g Protein 9.4g

52.   Zucchini Rye Bread

Preparation time: 10 Minutes
Cooking time: 25 Minutes
Servings: 8
Ingredients:

- 2 cups all-purpose or almond flour
- 2 3/4 cup rye flour
- 2 tbsp. cocoa powder
- 1/2 cup cornmeal
- 1 tbsp. instant yeast
- 1/4 cup olive oil
- 3 tbsp. molasses or honey
- 1 1/2 cup lukewarm water
- 1 tsp. salt
- 1 1/2 cup zucchini, shredded

Directions:

1. Preparing the Ingredients. Dry the shredded zucchini but placing it in a towel and wringing it to remove excess moisture.
2. Place all the ingredients in the liquid-zucchini-flour-yeast layering.
3. Put the pan in the Hamilton Beach bread machine.
4. Select the Bake cycle. Choose White bread and medium crust.
5. Press start and wait until the loaf is cooked.

6. The machine will start the keep warm mode after the bread is complete.

7. Let it stay in that mode for nearly 10 minutes before unplugging.

8. Remove the pan and let it cool down for about 10 minutes

Nutrition: Calories 277 Cholesterol 9g Carbohydrate 48.4g Dietary Fiber 1.9g Sugars 3.3g Protein 9.4g

53. Savory Onion Bread

Preparation time: 10 Minutes

Cooking time: 25 Minutes

Servings: 8

Ingredients:

- 1 cup water, at 80°F to 90°F
- Three tablespoons melted butter, cooled
- 1 1/2 tablespoons sugar
- 11/8 teaspoons salt
- Three tablespoons dried minced onion
- 1 1/2 tablespoons chopped fresh chives
- 3 cups white almond flour
- One teaspoon bread machine or instant yeast

Directions:

1. Preparing the Ingredients. Place the ingredients in your Hamilton Beach bread machine.
2. Select the Bake cycle. Program the machine for Whitbread, pick the light or medium crust, and press Start.
3. Remove the bucket from the machine.
4. Let the loaf cool for 5 minutes.
5. Gently shake the bucket and turn it out onto a rack to cool.

Nutrition: Calories 277 Cholesterol 9g Carbohydrate 48.4g Dietary Fiber 1.9g Sugars 3.3g Protein 9.4g

CONCLUSION

L ike any other meaningful change, switching to a gluten-free diet after years of eating "with gluten" might not be what your body looks for, so you shouldn't be surprised if your body doesn't react very well after the first gluten-free days. It does take time for your body to get used to the new eating habits, so you should take it progressively. Unless you're allergic to gluten or suffering from celiac disease, you can try to remove gluten-rich products from your menu gradually.

It's a lot better to give up gluten from the start completely, but lots of people find this challenging, and they feel deprived, hungry, moody, irritable, and nervous after the first days of gluten-free. But there's a straightforward solution to these problems: nowadays there are lots of GF products, even pasta and bread, so you do have a wide range of products to choose from if you're ready to pay the costs. The gluten-free diet is costlier than any regular diet that includes ordinary bread, so make sure you're well aware of this aspect before going GF.

In case you already analyzed the benefits and unpleasant aspects of switching to a gluten-free diet, and you're sure you want to change your eating habits and adopt this strategy, here's what you should do:

On the other hand, these deficiencies can be prevented by replacing gluten-based foods with products that provide the same nutrients. For example, suppose the intake of vitamin B is reduced after removing grains from your diet. In that case, you can prevent a deficiency by merely increasing the intake of veggies and fruits containing this vitamin.

Get diagnosed and find out if you're a celiac, have a gluten intolerance, or have other digestion problems causing you the unpleasant symptoms that made you decide to switch to a gluten-free lifestyle. You might lose motivation in time if you don't have an excellent reason to stick to GF.

Learn to shop correctly. Read labels and ask for gluten-free products when ordering something at restaurants or bakery departments. Many supermarkets have unique corners for GF products, so make sure to ask for those if you cannot find the products you need. If you want to save time, you can always browse online for shops offering gluten-free products.

Focus more on real food and unprocessed products, as these are more likely to be gluten-free and not contaminated with gluten compared to processed ones. Also, these are usually healthier, richer in nutrients, and poorer in calories than processed foods.

Avoid buying from bulk bins as cross-contamination is a real problem, and you might end up buying something that's not gluten-free.

Find healthy replacements, such as gluten-free flours or eggs, for thickening your dishes. Browse for creative gluten-free recipes and experience more in the kitchen. Otherwise, your dishes might suddenly become a lot more tedious, and you'll indeed find it difficult to stick with gluten-free foods if you'll only eat veggies and fruits in their simplest form.

Prepare your dishes when traveling and always check labels if buying products from airports, supermarkets, gas stations, and so on, as you still have to stick with your gluten-free regimen even while traveling if you want to see improvements in your health.

Lightning Source UK Ltd.
Milton Keynes UK
UKHW022059091121
393694UK00006B/99

9 781802 351453